Developing Num

CALCULATIONS

ACTIVITIES FOR THE DAILY MATHS LESSON

year 1

Peter Patilla

A & C BLACK

Contents

Reprinted 2002, 2004, 2005, 2006
Published 2002 by A&C Black Publishers Limited
38 Soho Square, London W1D 3HB
www.acblack.com

ISBN-10: 0-7136-6062-7
ISBN-13: 978-0-7136-6062-3

Editor: Lucy Poddington

The author and publishers would like to thank Madeleine Madden and Corinne McCrum for their advice in producing this series of books.

A CIP catalogue record for this book is available from the British Library.

A & C Black uses paper produced with elemental chlorine-free pulp, harvested from managed sustainable forests.
Printed in Great Britain by Caligraving Ltd, Thetford, Norfolk.

Introduction

Developing Numeracy: Calculations is a series of seven photocopiable activity books designed to be used during the daily maths lesson. They focus on the second strand of the National Numeracy Strategy Framework for teaching mathematics. The activities are intended to be used in the time allocated to pupil activities; they aim to reinforce the knowledge, understanding and skills taught during the main part of the lesson and to provide practice and consolidation of the objectives contained in the framework document.

Year 1 supports the teaching of mathematics by providing a series of activities which develop important calculation skills. On the whole the activities are designed for children to work on independently, although due to the young age of the children, the teacher may need to read the instructions with the children and ensure that they understand the activity before they begin working on it.

Year 1 encourages children to:

- understand the operations of addition and subtraction, and to use the related vocabulary;
- know that addition can be done in any order;
- use the signs +, – and =, and recognise the use of symbols to stand for unknown numbers;
- recognise that more than two numbers can be added together;
- learn by heart all pairs of numbers with a total of 10;
- learn by heart addition and subtraction facts for pairs of numbers with a total of up to 10;
- learn by heart doubles of all numbers to at least 5;
- use a range of counting skills to calculate;
- identify and use near doubles;
- add 9 to single-digit numbers efficiently;
- use patterns of similar calculations and known facts to solve calculations;
- bridge through 10 and 20 when adding a single-digit number.

Extension

Many of the activity sheets end with a challenge (**Now try this!**) which reinforces and extends the children's learning, and provides the teacher with the opportunity for assessment. Again, it may be necessary to read the instructions with the children before they begin the activity. For some of the challenges the children will need to record their answers on a separate piece of paper.

Organisation

Very little equipment is needed, but it will be useful to have available: coloured pencils, counters, scissors, dice, number lines and number tracks. Providing 100-grids and 100-tracks allows children to extend the calculations on the sheet to include larger numbers. These resources can be found on pages 63 and 64.

Other useful counting equipment includes unit apparatus, such as interlocking cubes, and rod apparatus, such as number rods. To help children understand concepts and develop a wide range of mathematical language, they should have regular opportunities to use both unit and rod apparatus.

The activities in this book will naturally bring in elements of counting and problem solving. Children need to be confident and efficient with their counting to be able to develop their calculation skills effectively. They will need regular counting practice to consolidate and develop the skills outlined in the Numbers and the Number System strand of the Strategy for Year 1 (see **Developing Numeracy: Numbers and the Number System Year 1**).

To help teachers select appropriate learning experiences for the children, the activities are grouped into sections within this book. However, the activities are not expected to be used in that order; the sheets are intended to support, rather than direct, the teacher's planning.

Some activities are deliberately more challenging than others, to allow for the widely varying ability in most classrooms. Many activities can be made easier or more challenging by masking and substituting some of the numbers. You may wish to re-use some pages by copying them onto card and laminating them, or by enlarging them onto A3 paper.

Teachers' notes

Brief notes are provided at the foot of each page giving ideas and suggestions for maximising the effectiveness of the activity sheets. These can be masked before copying.

Calculation strategies

Children in Year 1 may use the following strategies when working out additions.

Count all Children count each set in ones, then find the total by re-counting from one. For example, 2 + 5 would be said as *one, two* followed by *one, two, three, four, five*; the total is then *one, two, three, four, five, six, seven.*

Count on Children count on either from the first number or the larger number to find the total. For example, 2 + 5 would be said as *two, three, four, five, six, seven* (counting from the first number) or *five, six, seven* (counting from the larger number).

Quick recall Children have enough experience to remember or quickly work out additions; answers are given fairly rapidly.

When working out subtractions, children may use the following strategies.

Count all Children count each set in ones. For example, 5 – 2 would be said as *one, two, three, four, five* followed by what is being taken away: *one, two.* The remainder is then *one, two, three.*

Count back Children count back to find the answer. For example, 5 – 2 would be said as *five, four, three.*

Quick recall Children have enough experience to remember or quickly work out subtractions; answers are given fairly rapidly.

During Year 1, children are expected to move towards quick recall strategies, learning most of the number facts within 10 by heart. For calculations between 10 and 20, they should be encouraged to use efficient counting strategies and apply known facts. Children should be steered towards using mental strategies rather than relying on counting aids such as counters or number lines.

Whole-class warm-up activities

The following activities provide some practical ideas which can be used to introduce the main teaching part of the lesson.

Unison response

Tie a small weight to the end of a piece of string and swing it like a pendulum. Say a starting number at the start of a swing, for example 3. The children add one to the number, responding in unison at the end of the swing. Repeat for other numbers, then practise subtracting one in the same way. As children grow more confident, ask them to add or subtract other numbers. If appropriate, you could ask them to respond on the half-swing, which allows less thinking time.

Show me

Provide each child with a set of 0 to 10 number cards, which they should arrange face up in front of them for quick and easy access. Say a calculation, for example *3 plus 2.* Clap your hands three times to allow the children time to work out the answer mentally. Immediately after the last clap, the children hold up the number card showing the answer. Over the course of the year, gradually reduce the time between claps to decrease the thinking time. The activity can also be done using larger numbers and 0 to 20 number cards.

What is the question?

Write a number on the board, such as 7, and explain that this is the answer to a calculation. Ask a child to come to the board and write any calculation which has the answer 7, for example 6 + 1. Draw a large box around the calculation. Ask other children to write more calculations with the answer 7. If a calculation is the same type as the one in the box (in this example, an addition) it should be written in the box. Otherwise it should go outside the box (you could draw another box for subtractions). In this way the pupils' responses are sorted into types of calculation.

Bingo

Give each child a number grid and several counters or cubes. Ask the children to solve a calculation and cover the answer on the grid, for example: *Cover the total of four and five.* You could also ask questions which have a range of possible answers, for example: *Cover two numbers that total 15.* Discuss the various answers given by the children.

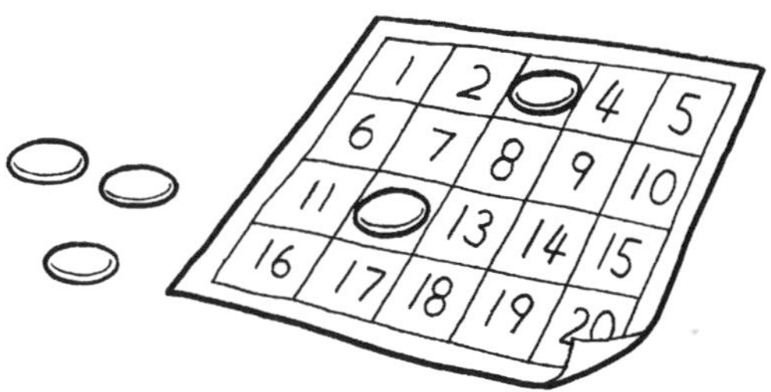

Silent response

Ask the children to sit with their eyes closed and their hands stretched out in front of them. Give a range of statements, some true and some untrue, for example: *The total of 3 and 4 is 8. The difference between 4 and 8 is even.* If the statement is true, the children should raise their hands in the air. If it is untrue, they should put their hands on their knees. You could clap your hands a short time after making the statement, to signal the moment when the children should respond.

Find the total

- **Write how many altogether.**

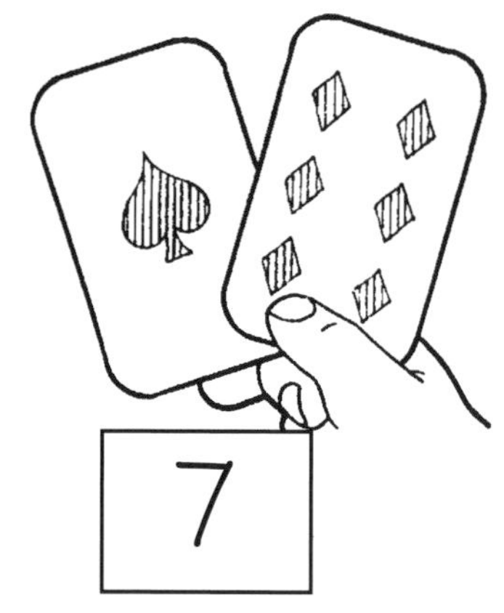

7

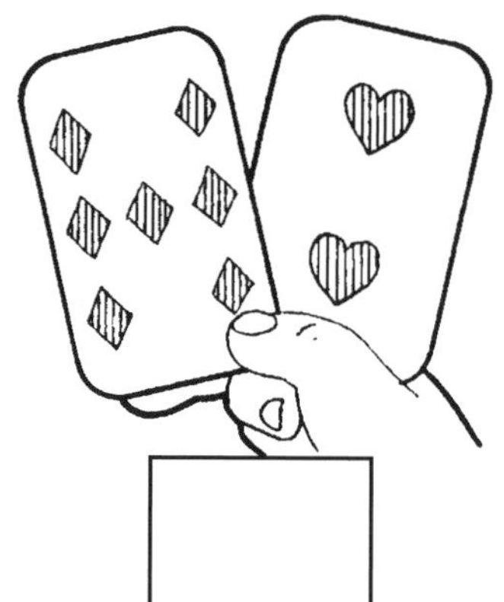

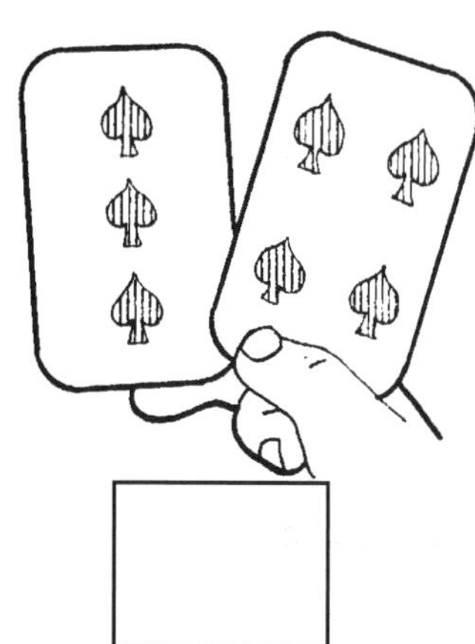

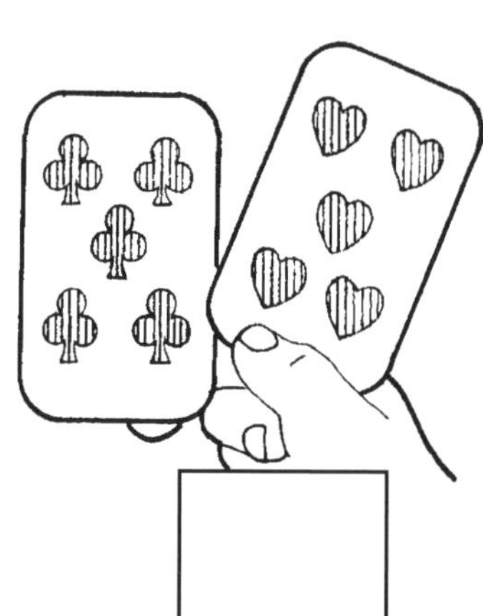

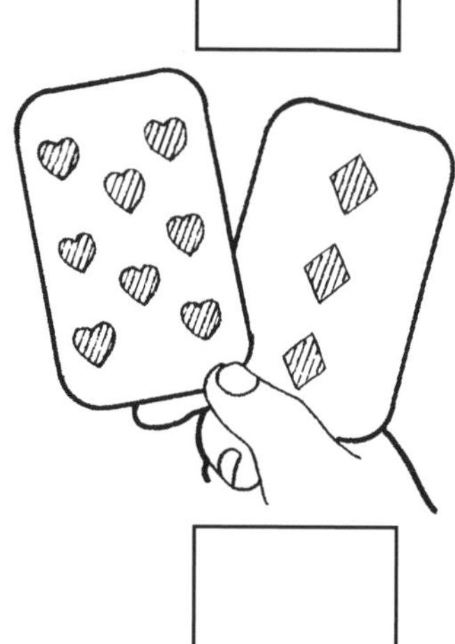

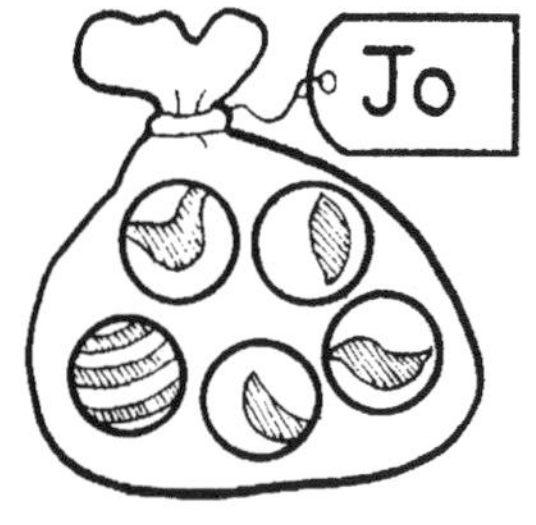

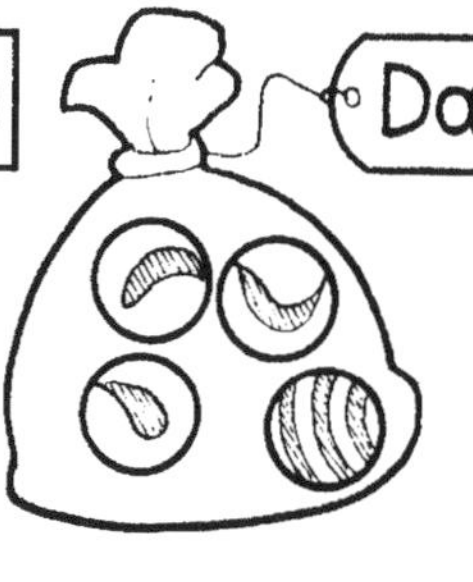

- **Write the total marbles for:**

Jo and Kate 

Emma and Dat 

Ben and Jo

How can the children make 9 marbles?

- **Write the names.** ______________________

Teachers' note Some children may be able to write the complete additions. For the extension activity, encourage the children to look for more than one solution by hinting that three children could make a total of nine marbles.

Adding factory

- **Choose how many go in.**
- **Write how many come out.**

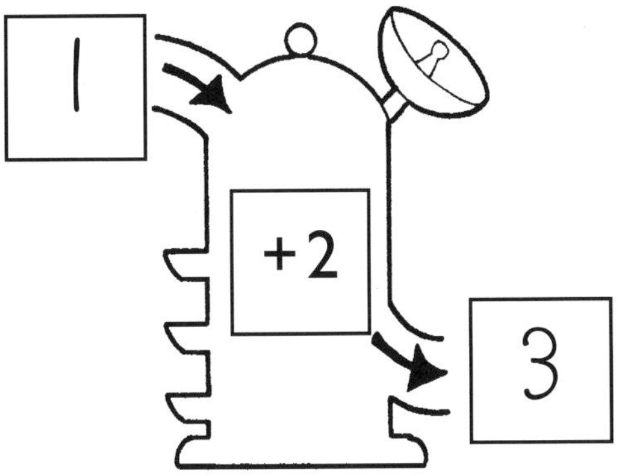

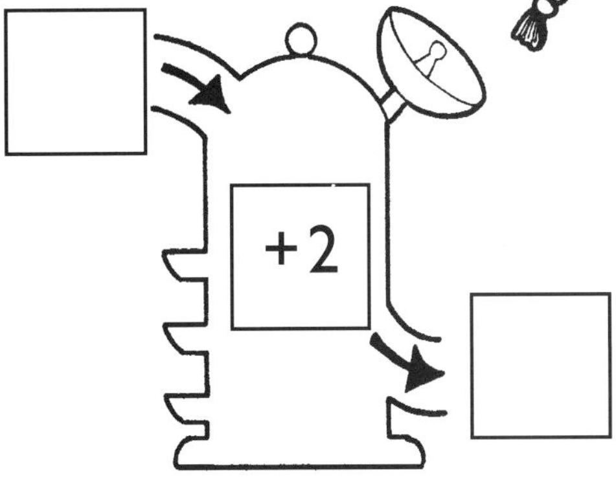

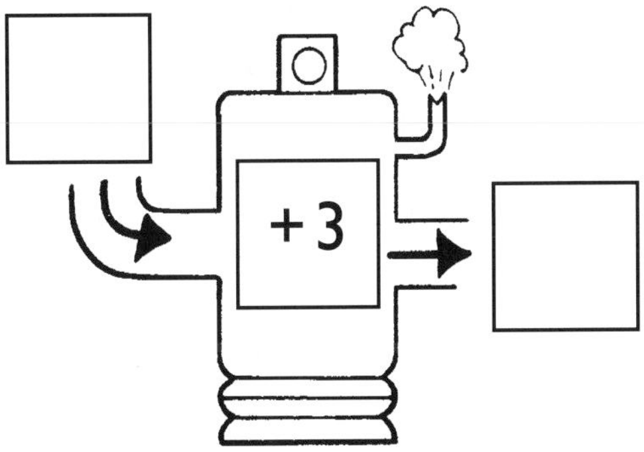

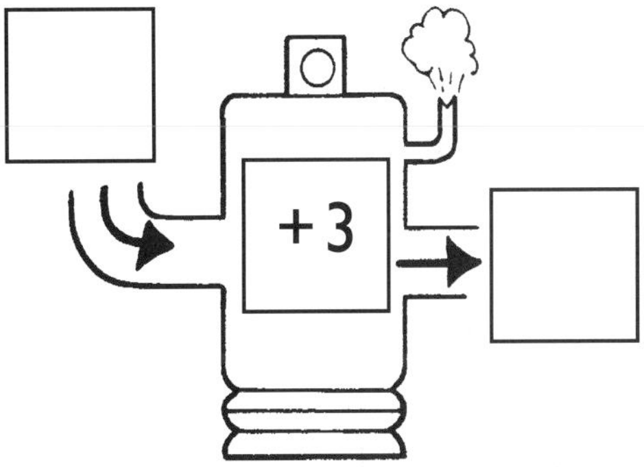

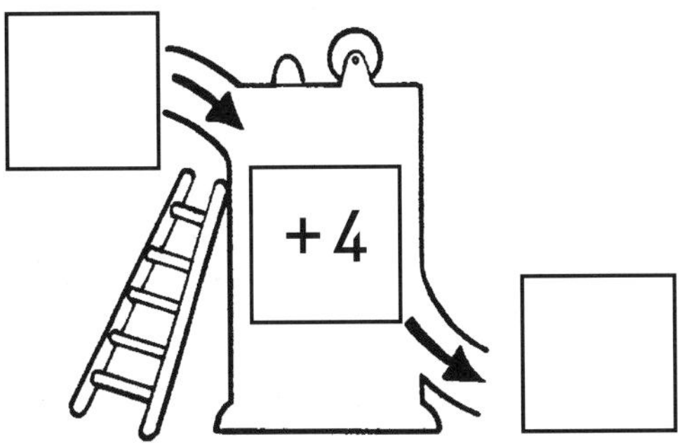

- **Put in numbers** greater than 10.
- **Write how many come out.**

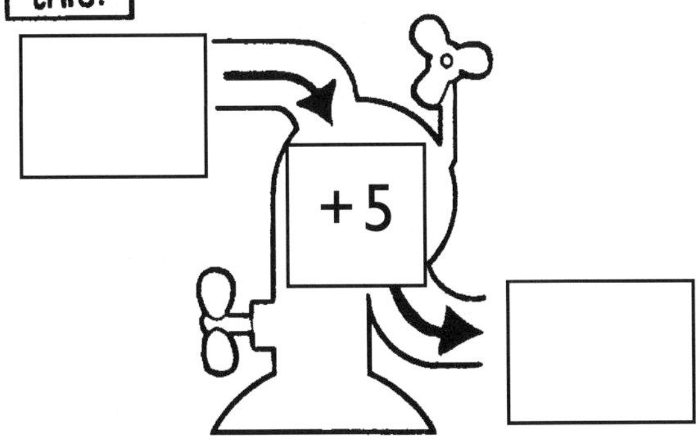

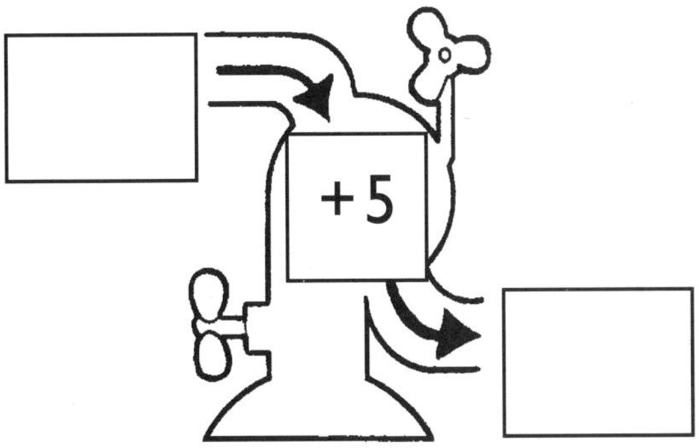

Teachers' note The children could use cubes as an aid. Encourage them to choose different numbers each time, and to try sequential numbers and look for patterns (you could provide extra copies of the sheet for them to extend the patterns). They could try some 'really hard' numbers. Ask how many must go into the machine for 10 (or another specified total) to come out.

The chocolate factory

• **Add the numbers. Write the total.**

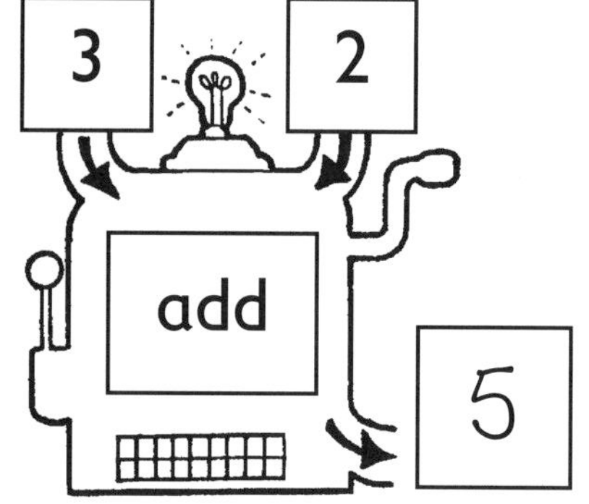

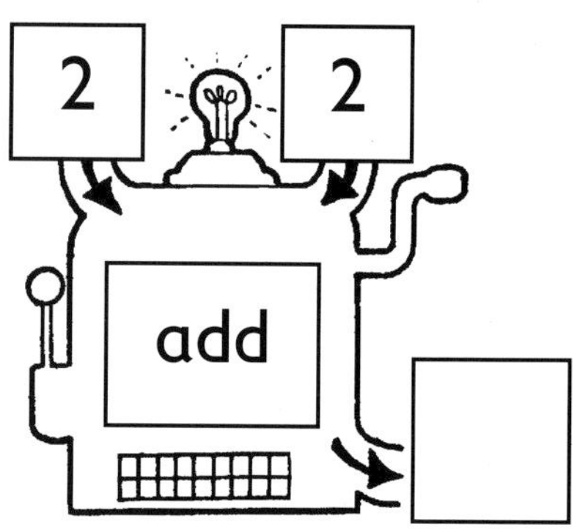

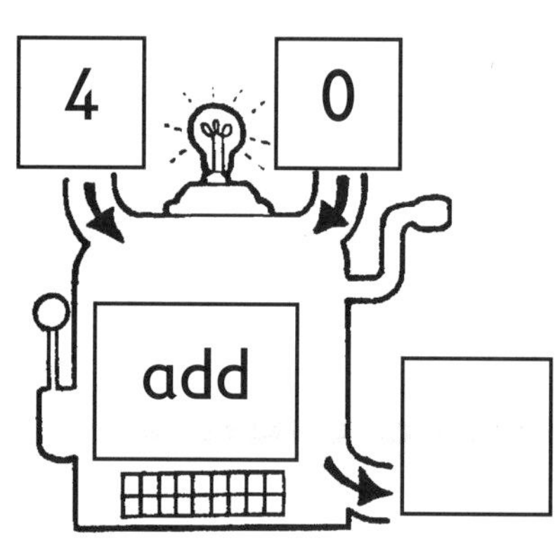

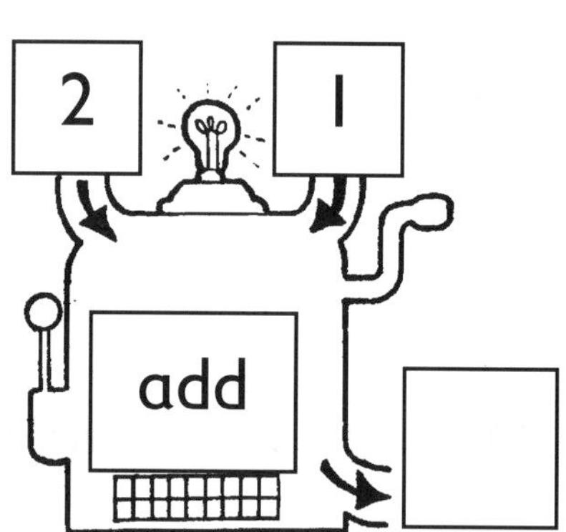

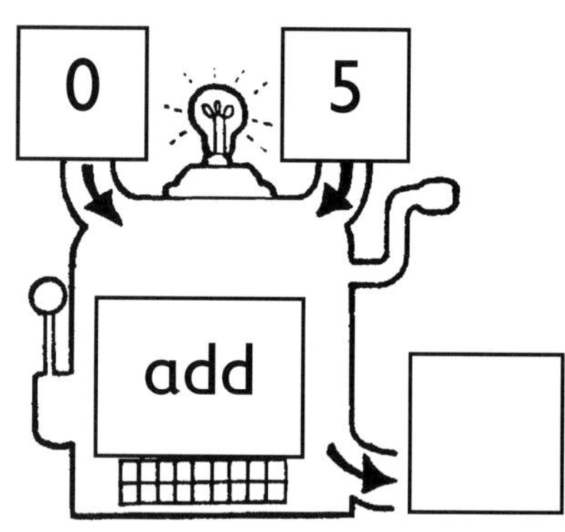

• **Make each chocolate box total 5.**

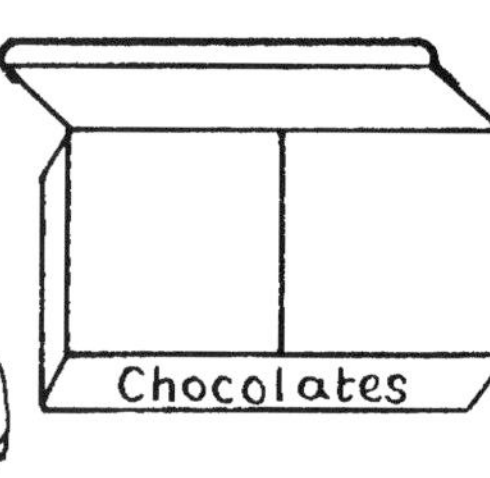

• **Choose your own total.**

Each chocolate box totals ☐.

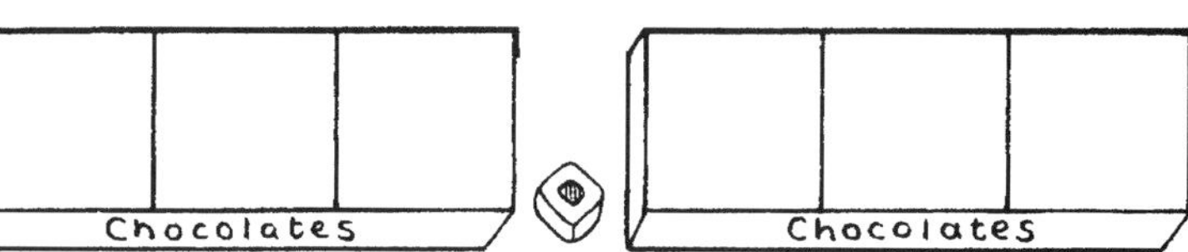

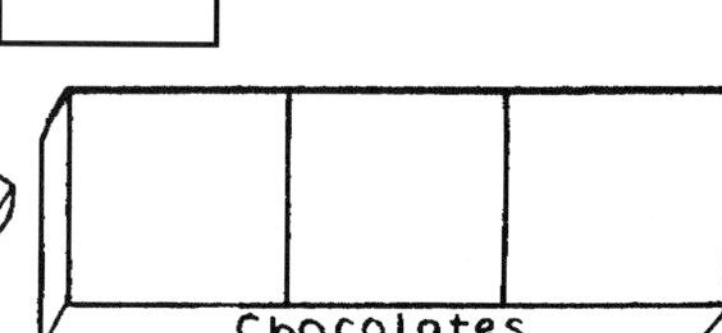

Teachers' note You could introduce this activity by playing 'Show me' (see page 5). Ensure that the children learn by heart all number facts with totals of up to five. Check the strategy they use for this activity. If they need to use counting aids, encourage them to try using quick recall in subsequent activities.

Fishy additions

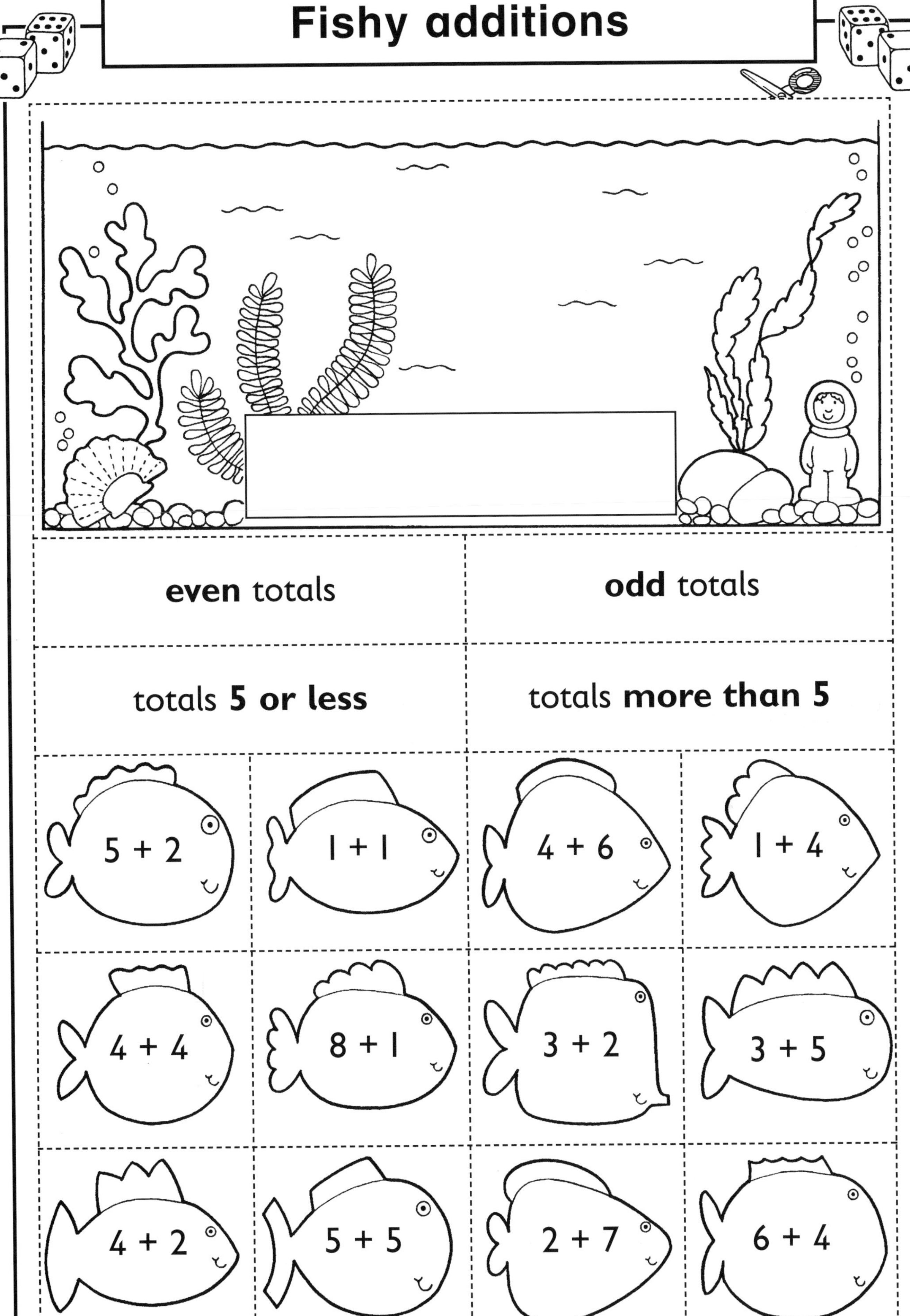

Teachers' note Cut out the cards. In pairs, the children should choose a label for the tank and place the correct fish in the tank. If necessary, revise odd and even numbers and provide paper for jottings. Discuss how counting on from the larger number is a quick way of adding. Explain that the order of adding does not matter (for example, 3 + 4 has the same answer as 4 + 3).

Minibeast totals

- **Join pairs of numbers to make 10.**

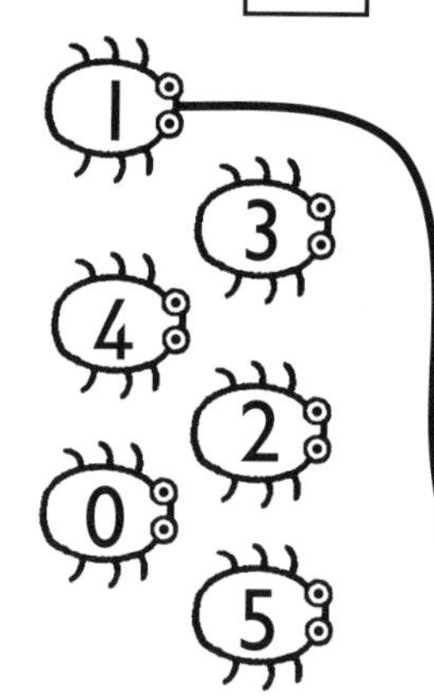

- **Write an addition for each pair.**

9 + 1 = 10 1 + 9 = 10

+ = 10

+ = 10

+ = 10

+ = 10 + = 10

+ = 10 + = 10

+ = 10 + = 10

- **Write the missing numbers to total 10.**

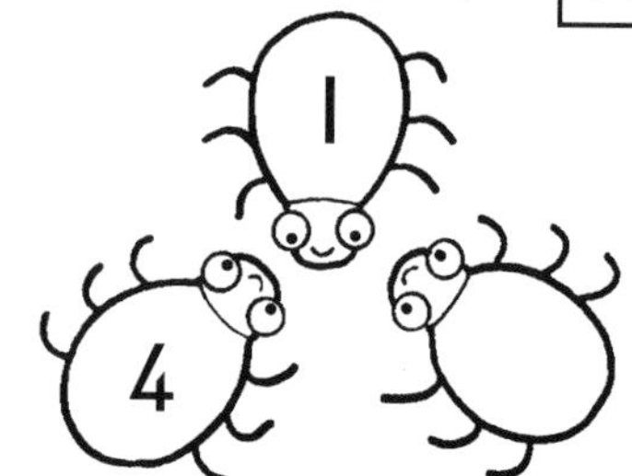

Teachers' note Ask the children to ring the two additions that are exactly the same (5 + 5 = 10). Ensure that the children learn by heart all the number pairs that total ten. Emphasise that the order of adding does not matter; this reduces the number of facts to be remembered. The pairs to be known are (10, 0), (9, 1), (8, 2), (7, 3), (6, 4) and (5, 5).

Addition race

- **Work out the answers as quickly as you can.**

5

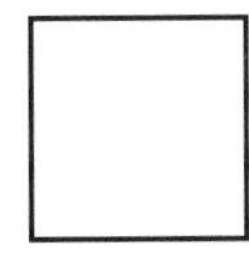

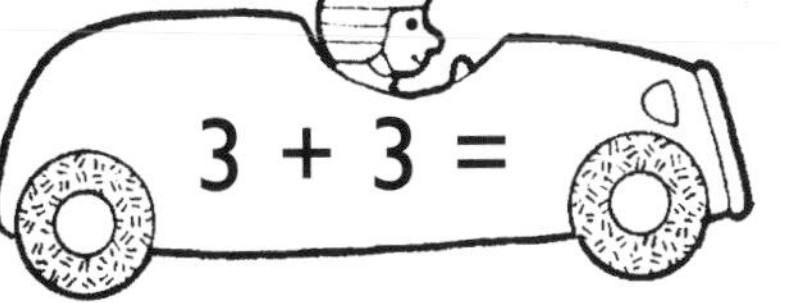

6 and 2 

4 plus 2 

The total of 4 and 6 

Add 5 to 2 

5 more than 1 

Double 5 

The sum of 3 and 5 

- **Write this addition in words.**

____

____

Teachers' note You could introduce this activity by playing 'Show me' (see page 5). Some children may require calculation aids such as number lines. Discuss with the children which facts they can do in their heads. Encourage mental methods of addition, in particular counting on from the larger number.

Bags of money!

• Write the total for each sack.

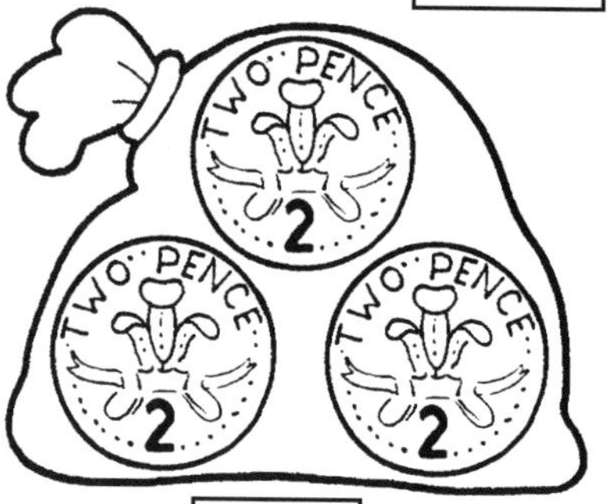

6 p

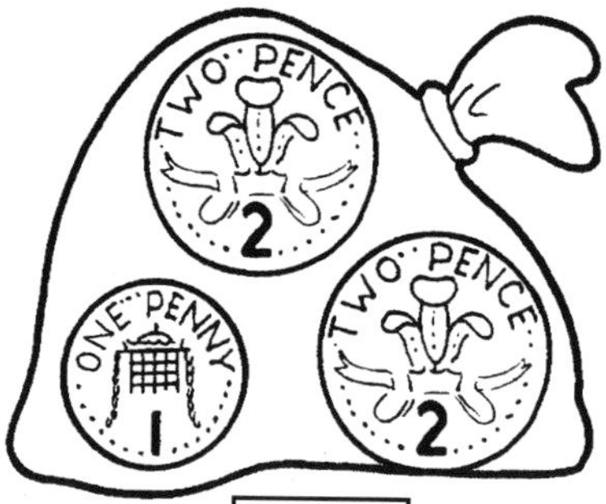

p

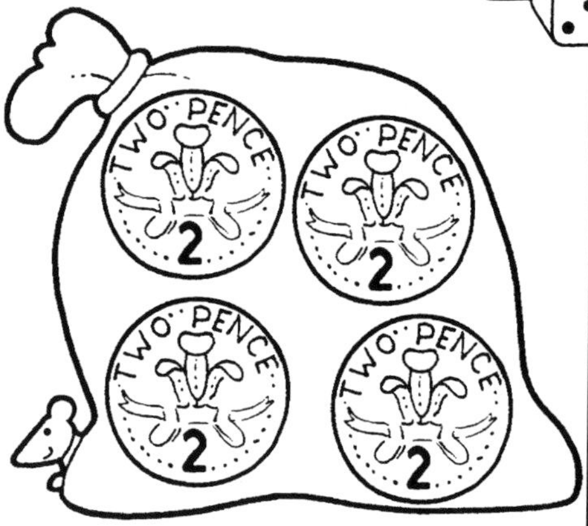

p

p

p

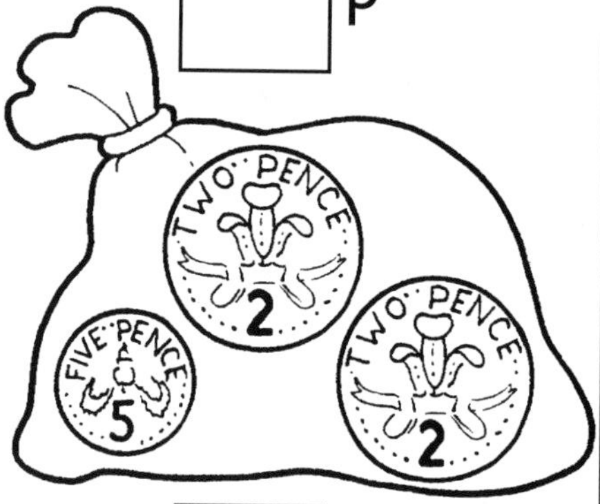

p

• Write the total cost.

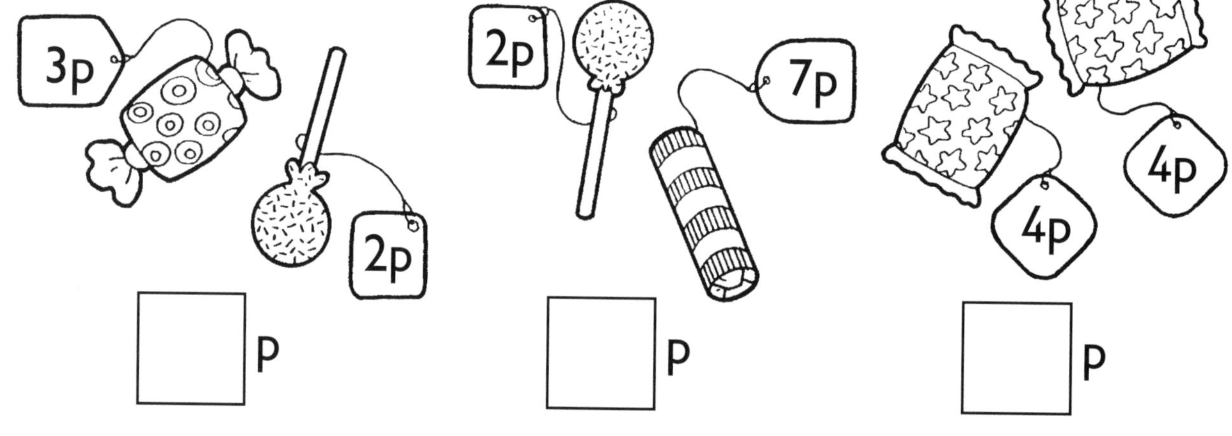

p

p

p

• Draw coins to total 10p.

Teachers' note Discuss which strategies the children use, and challenge them to manage without a number line. Encourage mental methods of addition, such as counting on from the coin of the highest value. The children can explore different ways of making a value such as 10p. They could investigate totals to 10p, including which totals can be made with two coins and which cannot.

Adding wordsearch

- **Write the answers in words.**

2 + 0 = two

3 + 7 = ____________

5 + 3 = ____________

1 + 2 = ____________

0 + 4 = ____________

3 + 2 = ____________

1 + 6 = ____________

4 + 5 = ____________

- **Now find the words in the wordsearch.**

s	t	w	o	g	a	p	t
v	w	f	o	u	r	d	i
m	g	d	n	i	n	e	a
s	t	e	n	p	k	l	g
y	a	e	s	e	v	e	n
e	i	g	h	t	f	i	v
f	o	t	h	r	e	e	y
o	f	n	e	f	i	v	e

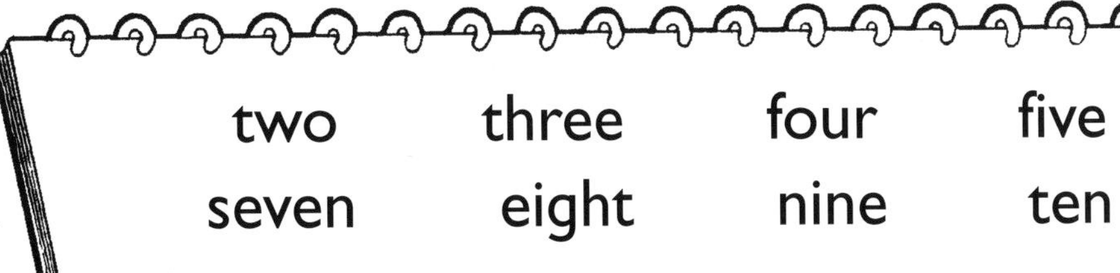

two three four five
seven eight nine ten

Teachers' note The number words are written horizontally in the grid. If appropriate, you could mask the word-bank at the bottom of the page.

Mystery numbers

- **Write the answers as words.**
- **Read down the grid to find the mystery number.**

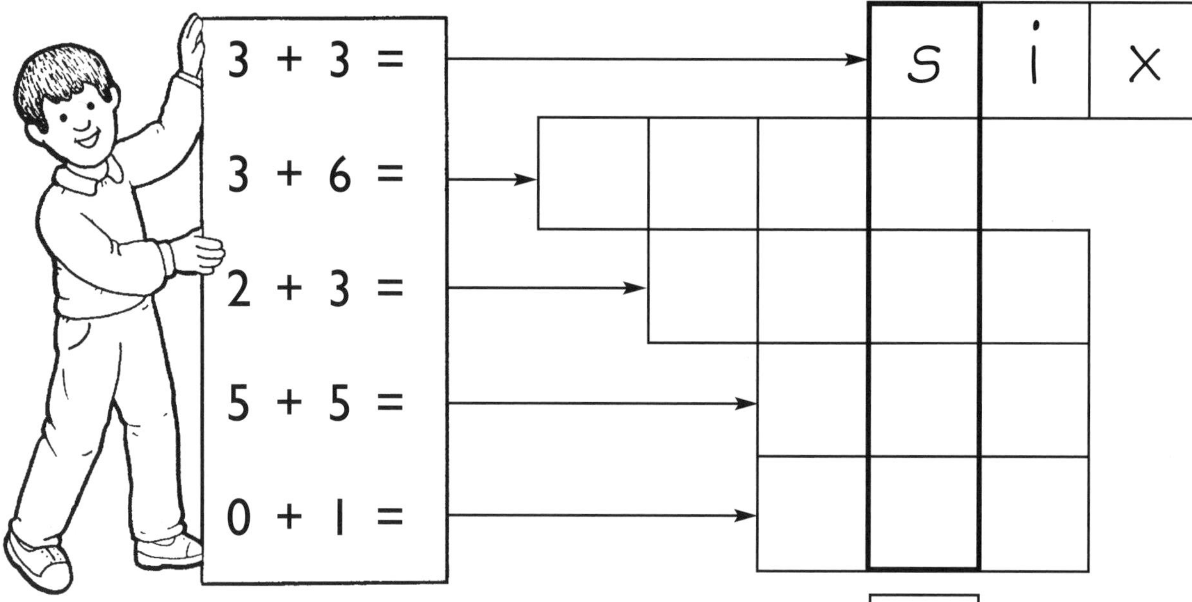

The mystery number is ☐.

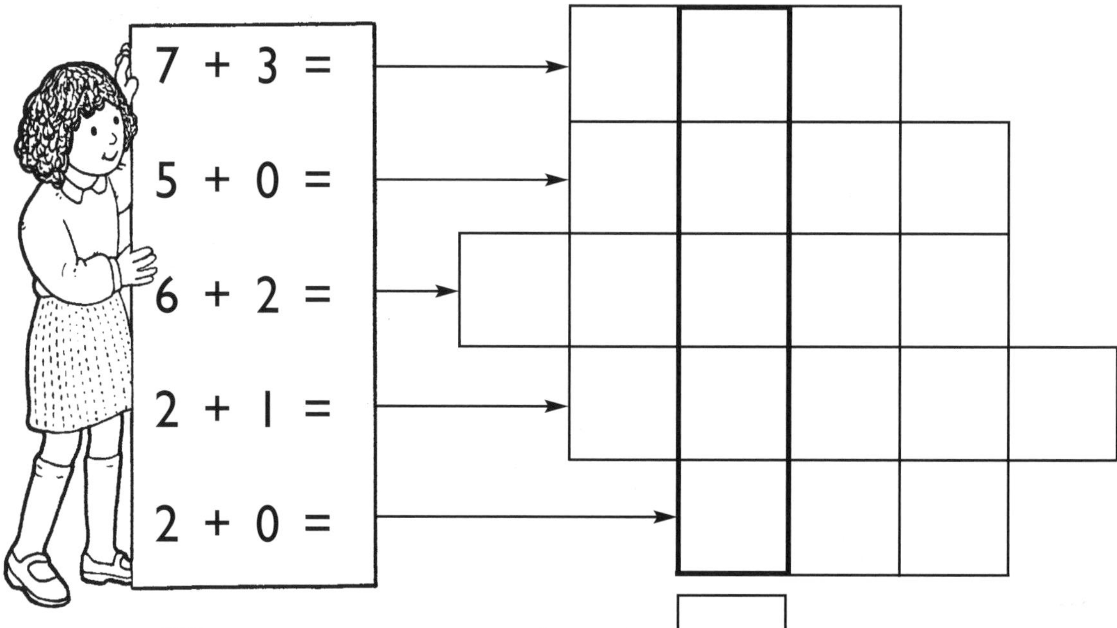

The mystery number is ☐.

- **Write your own addition to match each mystery number.** ____ + ____ = ____

Teachers' note If necessary, display the number words one to ten for reference. Remind the children to write one letter in each square and check which strategies the children use to work out the answers. For the extension activity, you could encourage the children to try 'really hard' additions. See also the note on page 35.

Naughty spiders

- **Write the hidden numbers on the spiders.**

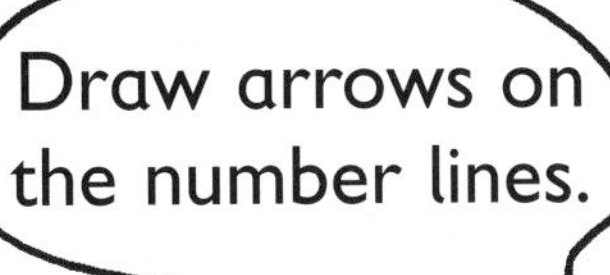

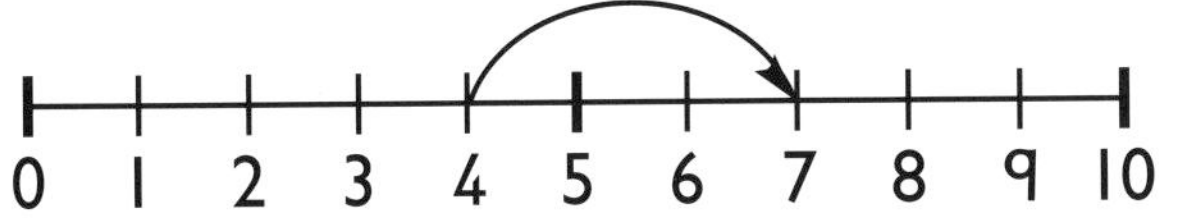

4 + 3 = 7

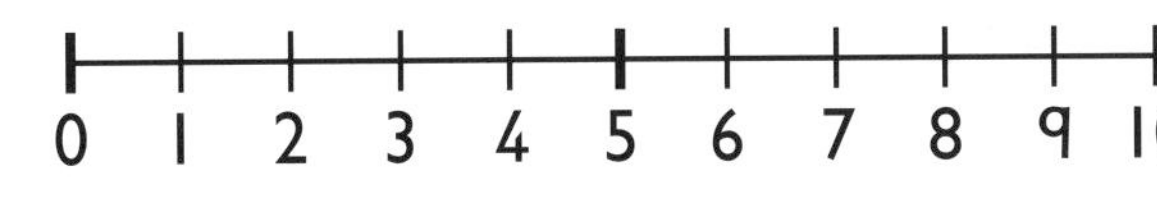

2 + ☐ = 6

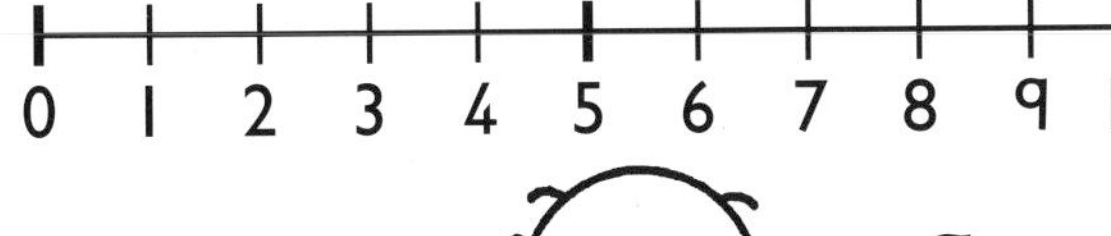

5 + ☐ = 9

0 1 2 3 4 5 6 7 8 9 10

8 + ☐ = 10

- **Write the hidden numbers.**

3 + ☐ = 10

4 + ☐ = 10

1 + ☐ = 6

5 + ☐ = 6

3 + ☐ = 3

0 + ☐ = 8

- **Write the hidden numbers.**

3 + 1 + ☐ = 8

4 + 2 + ☐ = 10

Teachers' note This activity will help the children to realise that addition can be done in any order. Show the children how to count on from the first number to the total, keeping a tally of how many they have counted.

Hidden numbers

- **Write the hidden numbers on the flowers.**

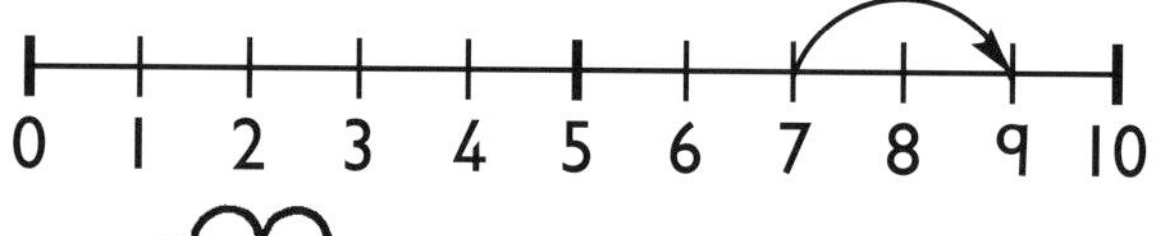

7 + 2 = 9

0 1 2 3 4 5 6 7 8 9 10

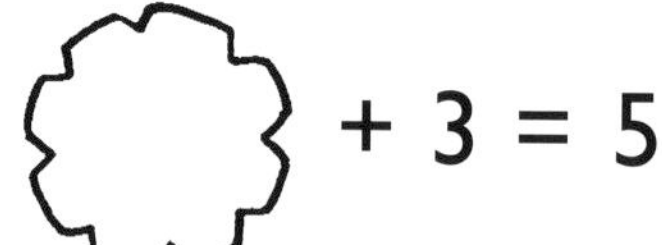

+ 3 = 5

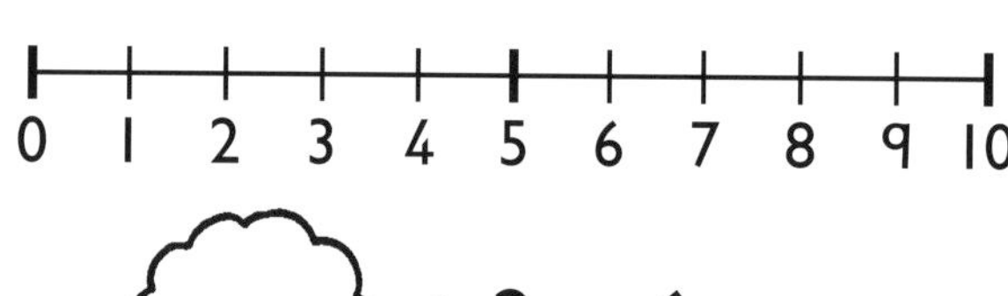

+ 2 = 6

0 1 2 3 4 5 6 7 8 9 10

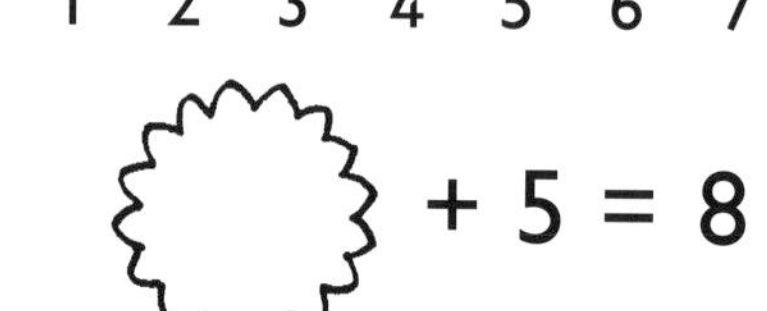

+ 5 = 8

- **Write the hidden numbers.**

+ 2 = 5

+ 5 = 8

+ 1 = 7

+ 0 = 5

+ 8 = 8

+ 6 = 10

- **Write the hidden numbers.**

+ 4 + 3 = 9

+ 2 + 1 = 7

Teachers' note This activity will help the children to realise that addition can be done in any order. Check which number facts they know by heart. In pairs, children could play a game with ten counters and a yoghurt pot. One child puts some of the counters under the pot and the other child works out how many are hidden. They can then swap roles and repeat.

Secret code

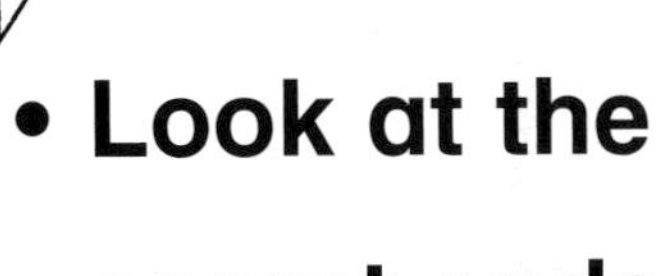

- **Look at the secret code.**

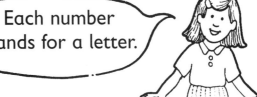

Each number stands for a letter.

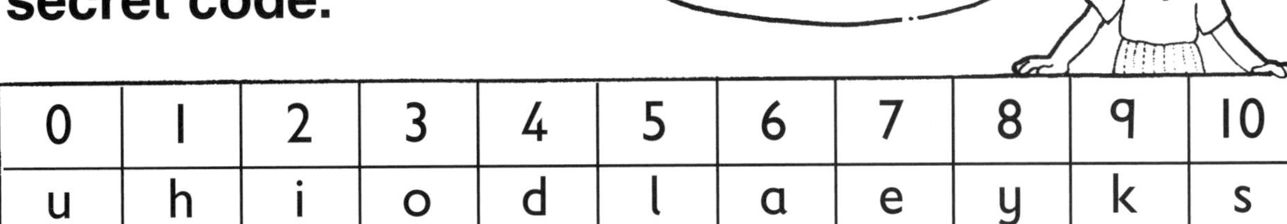

0	1	2	3	4	5	6	7	8	9	10
u	h	i	o	d	l	a	e	y	k	s

- **Answer all the additions.**
- **Use the code to find the message.**

2+2	3+0
4	

3+5	2+1	0+0

2+3	0+2	5+4	2+5

d ___ ___ ___ ___ ___ ___ ___ ___

0+1	1+2	3+2	2+0	1+3	5+1	2+6	7+3

___ ___ ___ ___ ___ ___ ___ ___ ?

- **Write the answer in code.**

+ =	+ =	+ =
y	e	s

Teachers' note Ensure that the children understand how to use the code grid. They could work in pairs to complete the activity.

Colour by numbers

- Colour yellow the shapes with a total of 5.
- Colour green the shapes with a total of 10.

2 + 8

3 + 2

4 + 6

10 + 0

0 + 5

1 + 9

0 + 10

5 + 5

1 + 4

9 + 1

2 + 3

7 + 3

4 + 1

3 + 7

5 + 0

8 + 2

6 + 4

Teachers' note If necessary, revise number pairs which total five and ten.

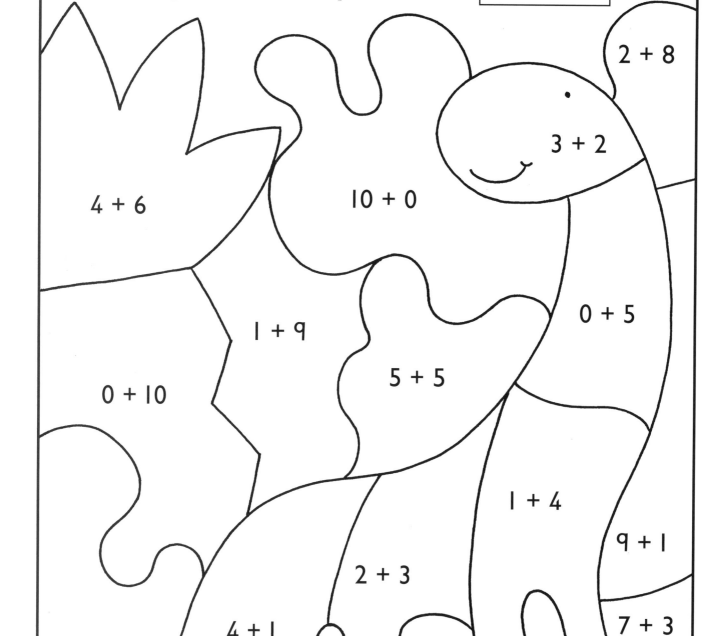

Rabbit warren

Rabbit is going to visit Mouse. She needs to find a path through the burrows with odd totals **.**

- **Write the answers. Then draw the path.**

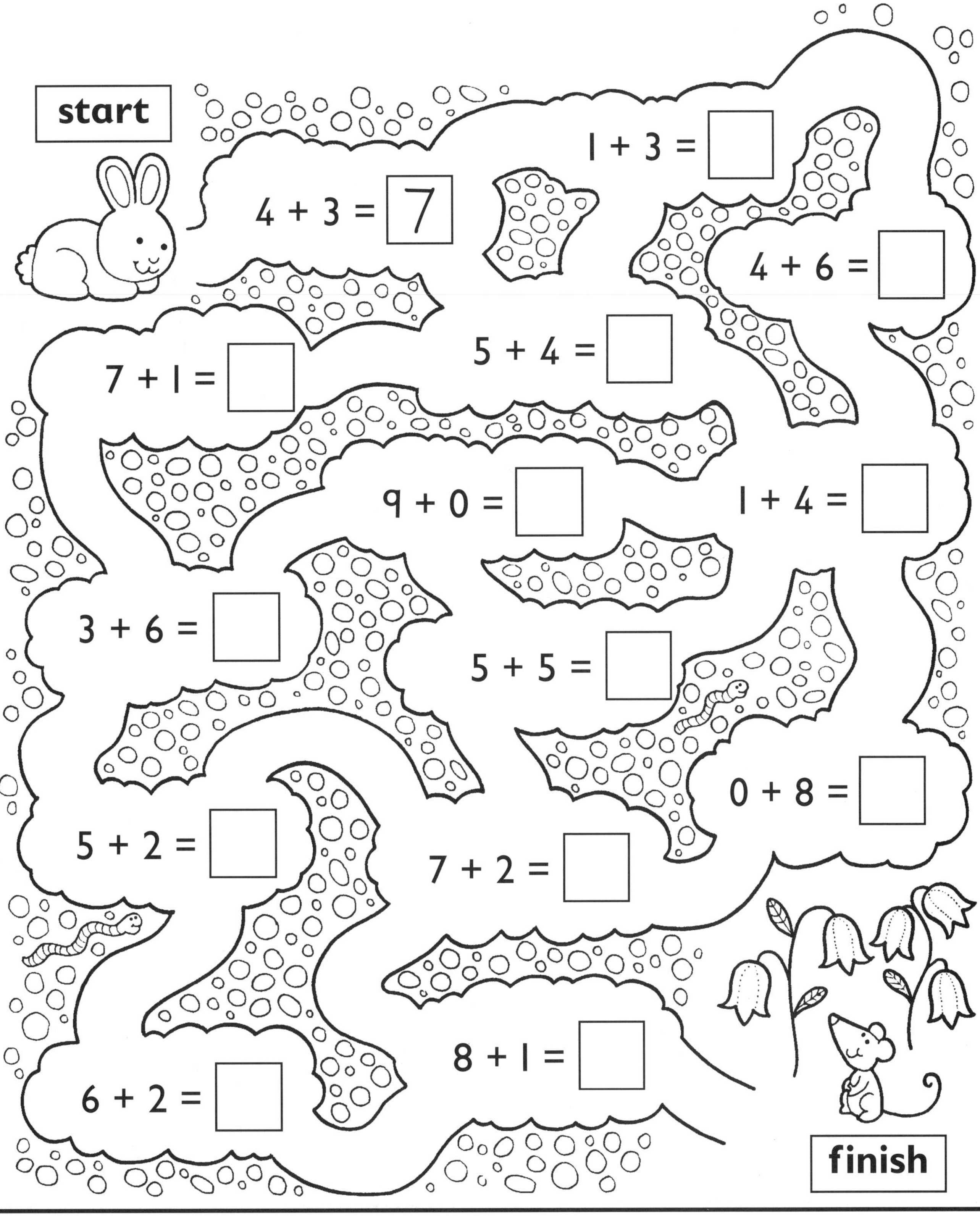

start

4 + 3 = 7

1 + 3 = ☐

4 + 6 = ☐

5 + 4 = ☐

7 + 1 = ☐

9 + 0 = ☐

1 + 4 = ☐

3 + 6 = ☐

5 + 5 = ☐

0 + 8 = ☐

5 + 2 = ☐

7 + 2 = ☐

8 + 1 = ☐

6 + 2 = ☐

finish

Teachers' note If necessary, revise odd and even numbers up to at least ten.

Addition sentences

Use 6, 4 and 10 to make different number sentences.	Use 3, 4 and 7 to make different number sentences.
Use 5, 4 and 9 to make different number sentences.	Use 5, 5 and 10 to make different number sentences.
Use 1, 5 and 6 to make different number sentences.	Use 3, 5 and 8 to make different number sentences.

1	2	3	4	5	6	7
8	9	10	5	0	add	

plus	equals	is	makes
altogether	the same as	+	
more than	totals	and	=

Teachers' note Provide one copy of the sheet for each pair of children to cut out the cards. In pairs, the children should choose an instruction card and make as many different number sentences as they can using the same set of three numbers. They may need to sort the cards first to match words with similar meanings. See page 32 for further instruction cards.

Subtracting factory

- **Choose how many go in.**
- **Write how many come out.**

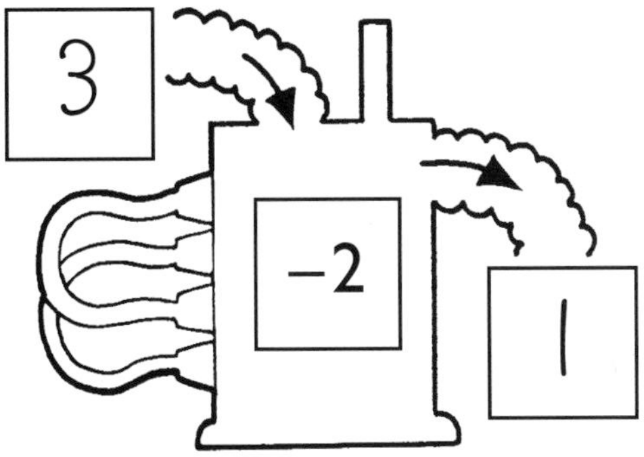

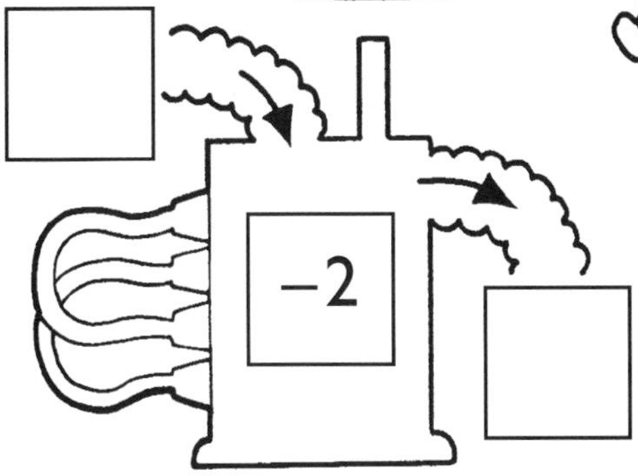

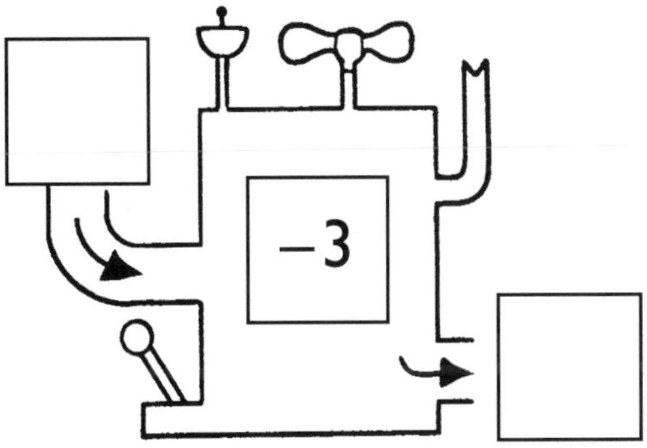

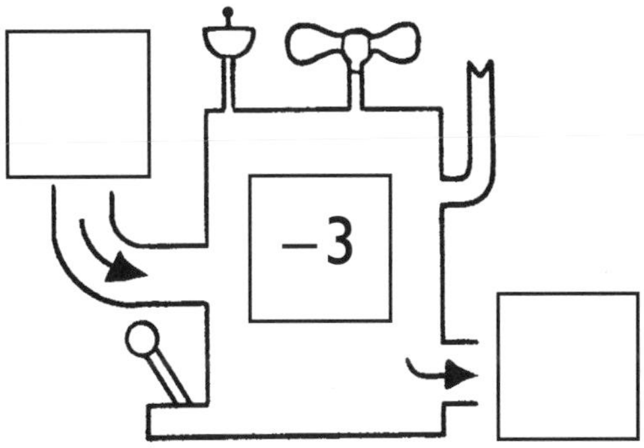

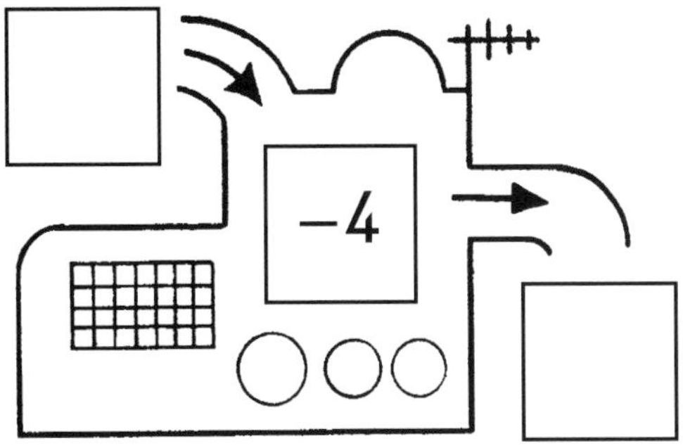

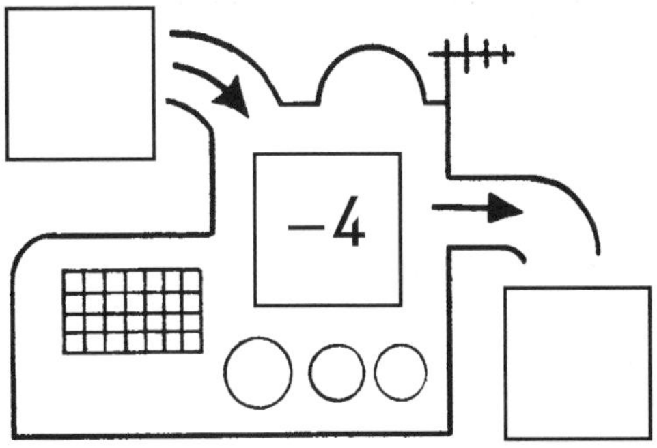

- **Put in numbers** greater than 10 .
- **Write how many come out.**

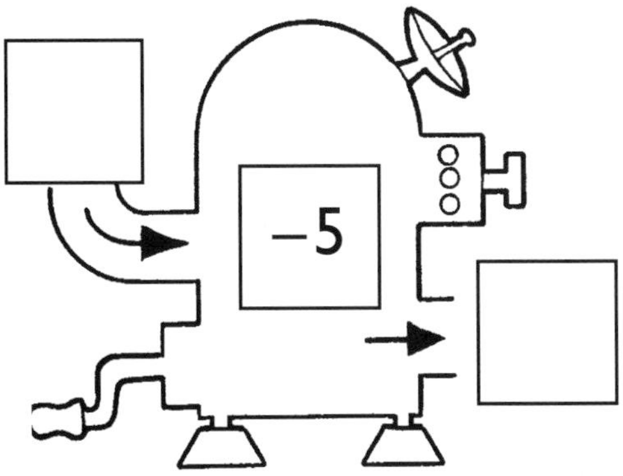

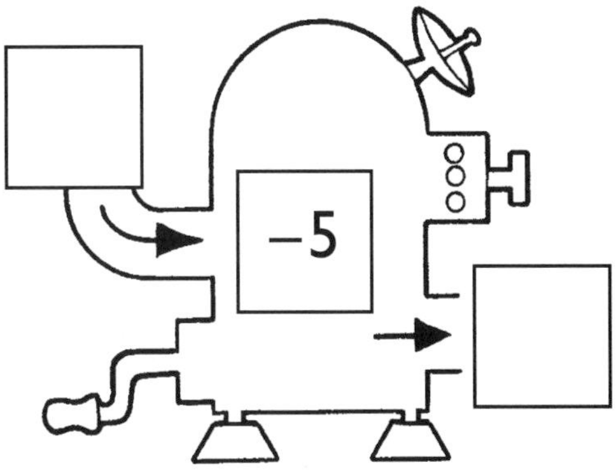

Teachers' note The children could use cubes to help them with this activity. Encourage them to choose different numbers for each machine, and to put in sequential numbers so that they can look for patterns (you could provide extra copies of the sheet for the children to extend the patterns). They could try entering some 'really hard' numbers.

The vegetable patch

- **Write the** difference **between the rows.**

the difference is 2

the difference is ☐

the difference is ☐

the difference is ☐

- **Write the** difference **between the shaded numbers.**

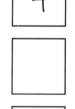

4

☐

☐

- **Write pairs of numbers which have a** difference of 4 **.**

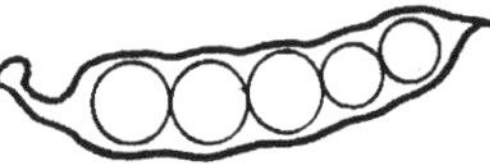

3 and 7 | ◯ and ◯ | ◯ and ◯

Teachers' note The word 'difference' sometimes causes problems for children. It can help to talk about 'number difference' to distinguish it from other differences such as colour, shape and size. Explain to the children that they can find the difference by counting on from the smaller number to the larger. Some children may need a number line for the extension activity.

To the bottom of the sea

- **Write the answers.**

Remember, – means take away.

10	10 – 0 = ☐	10 – 7 = ☐
9	10 – 1 = ☐	10 – 10 = ☐
8	10 – 2 = ☐	10 – 5 = ☐
7	10 – 3 = ☐	10 – 2 = ☐
6	10 – 4 = ☐	10 – 8 = ☐
5	10 – 5 = ☐	10 – 4 = ☐
4	10 – 6 = ☐	10 – 0 = ☐
3	10 – 7 = ☐	10 – 3 = ☐
2	10 – 8 = ☐	10 – 1 = ☐
1	10 – 9 = ☐	10 – 9 = ☐
0	10 – 10 = ☐	10 – 6 = ☐

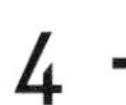

- **Write your own subtractions.**

9 – ☐ = ☐ 9 – ☐ = ☐ 9 – ☐ = ☐

Teachers' note The children could put counters on the number line (starting at 1) to help them. Encourage them to work down the page rather than across, and to notice a pattern in the first column. Discuss with the children how they worked out the answers; check whether they need counting aids and whether they know any of the facts by heart.

Alien space ships

- **Join each space ship to the correct number.**

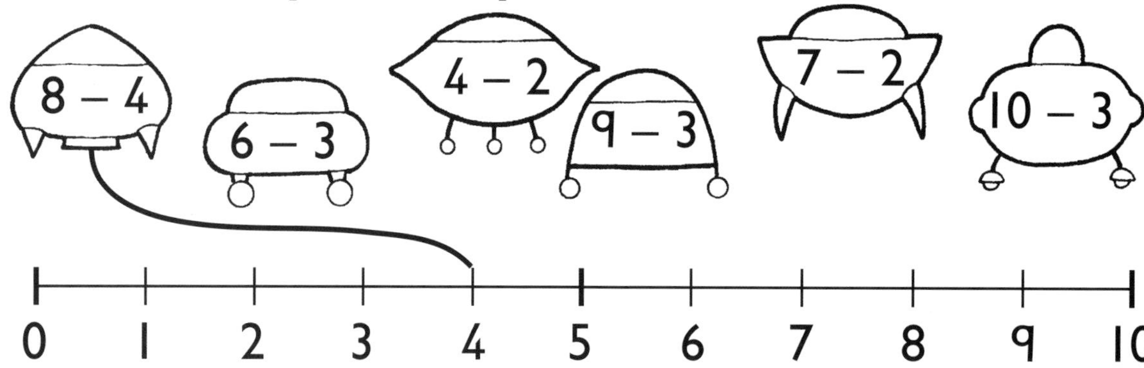

- **Write the answers.**

6 – 3 = ☐	5 – 2 = ☐	8 – 1 = ☐
9 – 5 = ☐	10 – 2 = ☐	6 – 0 = ☐

- **Write the answer on the alien's tummy.**

- **Write numbers on the space ships.**

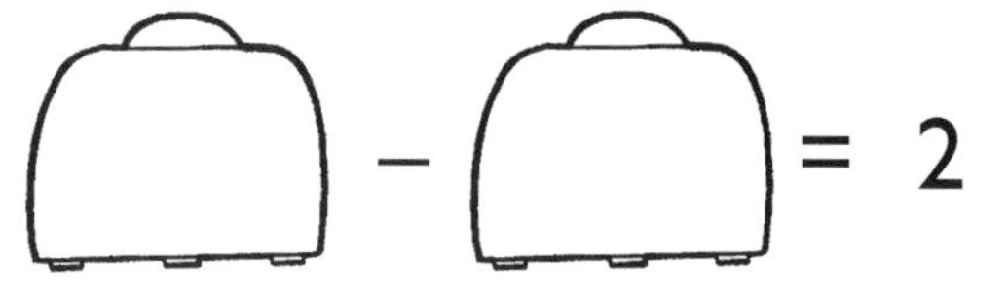

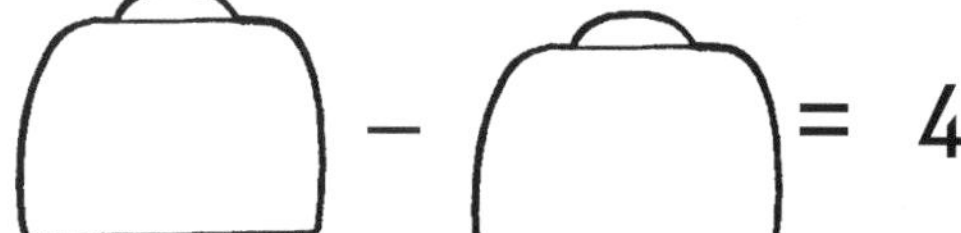

☐ – ☐ = 0

Teachers' note You could suggest that the children use a different colour for each space ship. Discuss with the children how they worked out the answers; check whether they need counting aids and whether they know any of the facts by heart. For the extension activity, encourage the children to find several different solutions for each subtraction. Challenge them to use large numbers.

Subtracting wordsearch

- **Write the answers in words.**

10 – 6 = four

10 – 0 = ______

8 – 3 = ______

10 – 2 = ______

10 – 1 = ______

6 – 3 = ______

9 – 3 = ______

10 – 3 = ______

- **Now find the words in the wordsearch.**

s	e	t	e	n	v	e	f
o	s	e	v	e	n	t	w
e	i	g	f	i	v	e	t
t	f	o	u	r	s	i	e
t	w	i	n	n	i	n	e
e	i	t	t	h	r	e	e
e	i	g	h	t	s	e	v
n	i	n	s	i	x	t	e

three four five

six seven eight nine ten

Teachers' note The number words are written horizontally in the grid. If appropriate, the word-bank at the bottom of the page could be masked. Encourage the children to make their own wordsearch with number words in a grid.

Shopping spree

• **Work out how much change from 10p.**

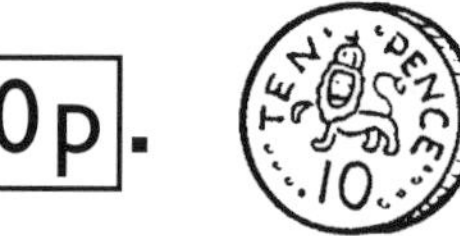

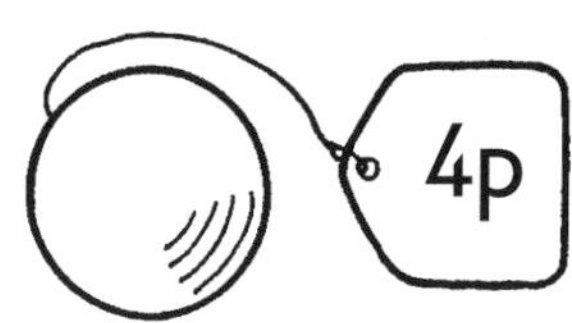

10p – 4 p = 6 p

10p – ☐ p = ☐ p

10p – ☐ p = ☐ p

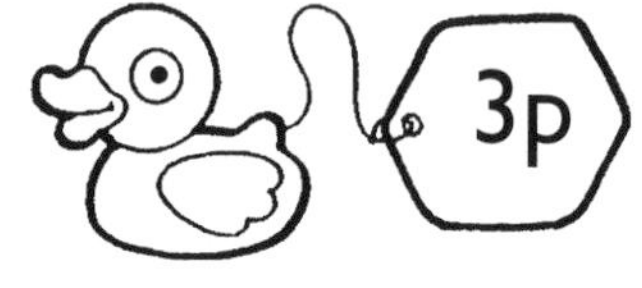

10p – ☐ p = ☐ p

• **Write how much change.**

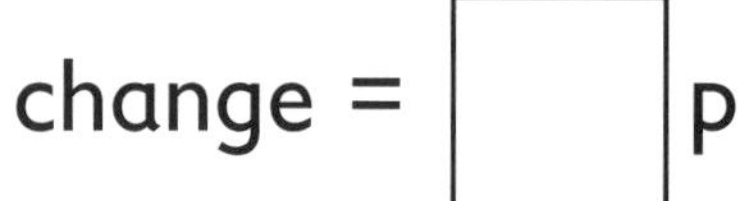

change = ☐ p

change = ☐ p

change = ☐ p

The coins show your change from 10p.

• **Write how much you spent.**

I spent ☐ p

I spent ☐ p

Teachers' note Ensure that the children are confident with changing 10p for equivalent amounts, and do not always change the 10p coin into ten 1p coins. In pairs, children could play a game with a set of coins totalling 10p and a yoghurt pot. One child puts some of the coins under the pot and the other child works out how much is hidden. They can then swap roles and repeat.

Kangaroo hops

You can use a number line to help you subtract.

5 − (3) = 2

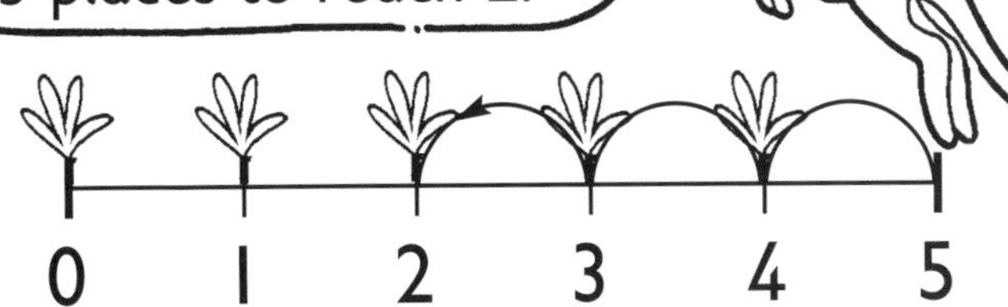

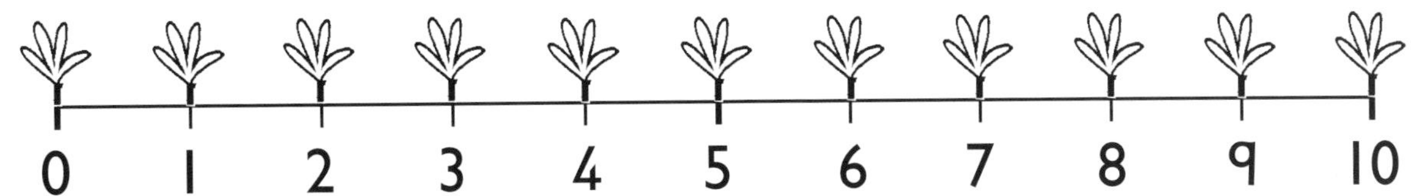

- **Write the missing numbers.**

7 − ( ) = 2 5 − ( ) = 1 8 − ( ) = 6

9 − ( ) = 3 10 − ( ) = 4 10 − ( ) = 8

- **Write a subtraction for each number line.**

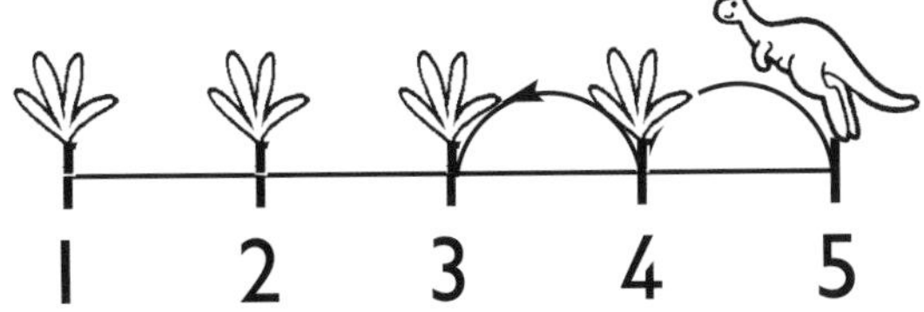

5 − ☐ = ☐

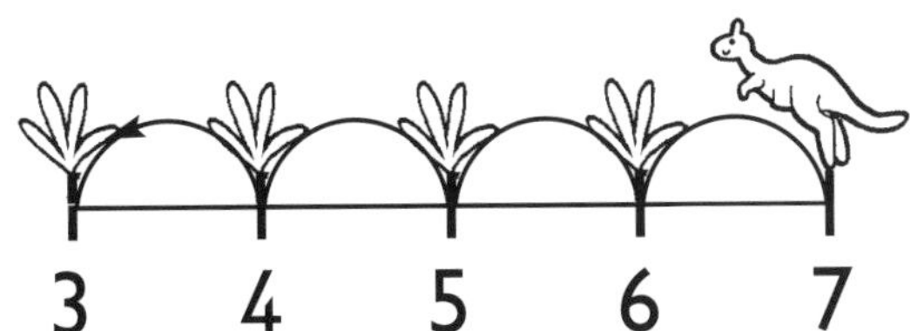

☐ − ☐ = ☐

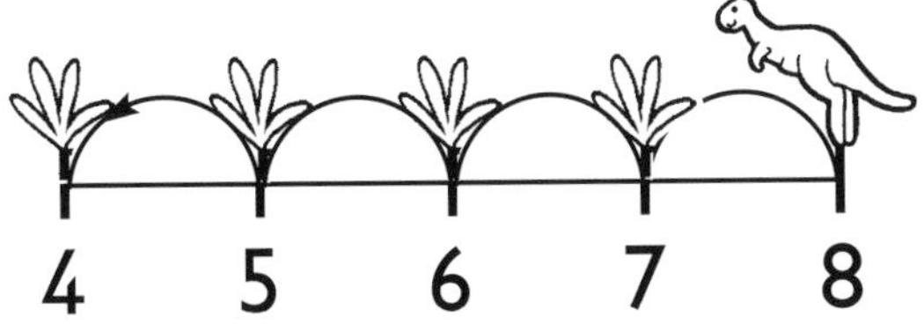

☐ − ☐ = ☐

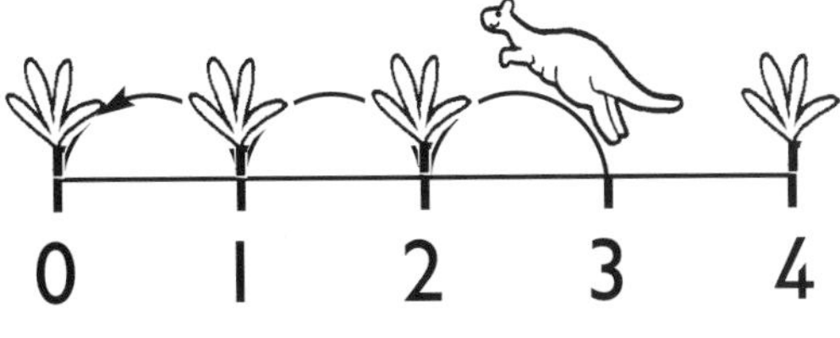

☐ − ☐ = ☐

Teachers' note Make sure children realise that in a subtraction of the type ☐−☐ = ☐ the first number is the starting point, the second number is what is taken away, and the third number is the result. Continued on page 28.

Down at the pond

You can use a number track to help you subtract.

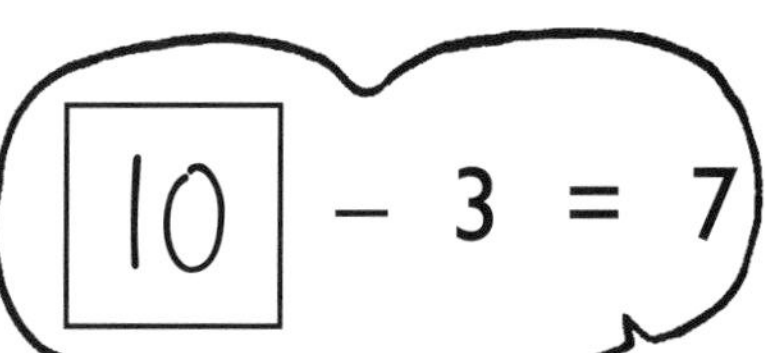

A jump back of 3 lands on 7.
10 must be the start.

0	1	2	3	4	5	6	7	8	9	10

- **Write the missing start numbers.**

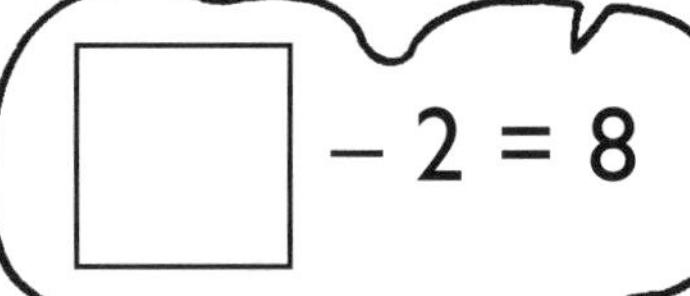

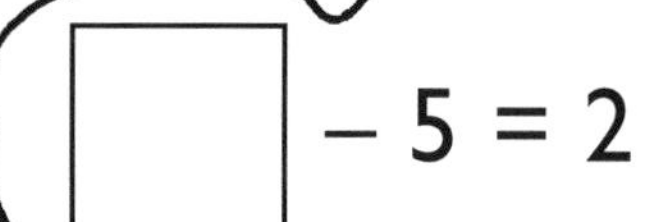

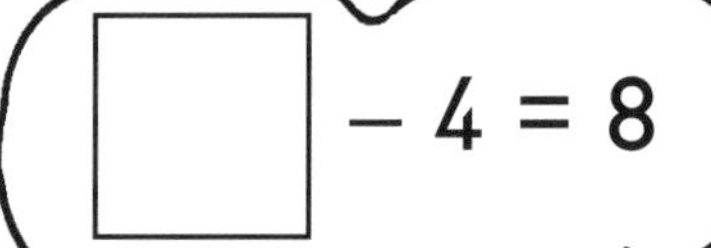

☐ – 3 = 6

- **Write the missing start numbers.**

6 are left.

There were  ducks. 3 swam away. 4 are left.

There were  ducks. 4 swam away. 5 are left.

Teachers' note Continued from page 27. Demonstrate the concept with a number line made up of children holding number cards. Give the children a subtraction, such as 6 – 1 = 5, and ask one child to be the kangaroo or frog and jump along the line. Then ask the children in the number line who has the start number, who has the number taken away and who has the result.

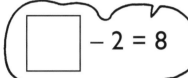

Farmyard code

- **Look at the code.**

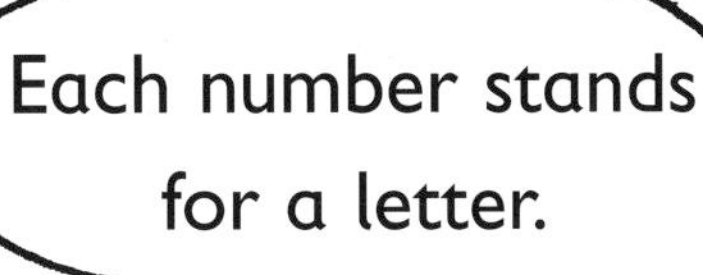
Each number stands
for a letter.

0	1	2	3	4	5	6	7	8	9	10
g	u	d	o	k	p	c	h	i	n	e

- **Answer the subtractions.**
- **Use the code to find the mystery animals.**

9–2	10–0	10–1
7		

h ___ ___

4–2	6–5	7–1	8–4

___ ___ ___ ___

8–3	9–1	0–0

___ ___ ___

9–3	10–3	10–2	8–2	7–3

___ ___ ___ ___ ___

Now
try
this!

- **Write number clues to spell out** dog.

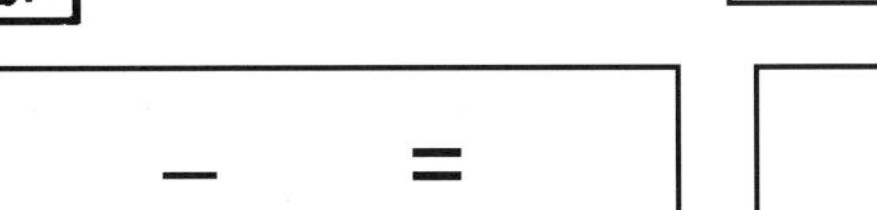

– =	– =	– =
d	o	g

Teachers' note The children could work in pairs. They can use the numbers on the stable doors as a number track to help with the subtractions. For the extension activity, suggest that they find the answer number first. As a further extension, the children could make up their own code and clues for zoo animals.

Fire engines

- **Write all the answers.**
- **Join each fire engine to the correct fire station.**

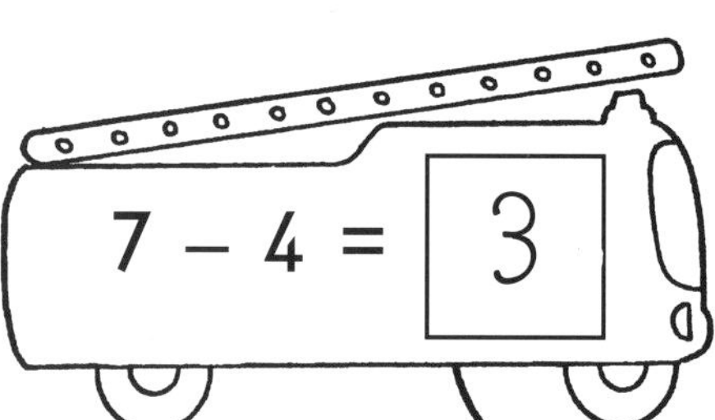

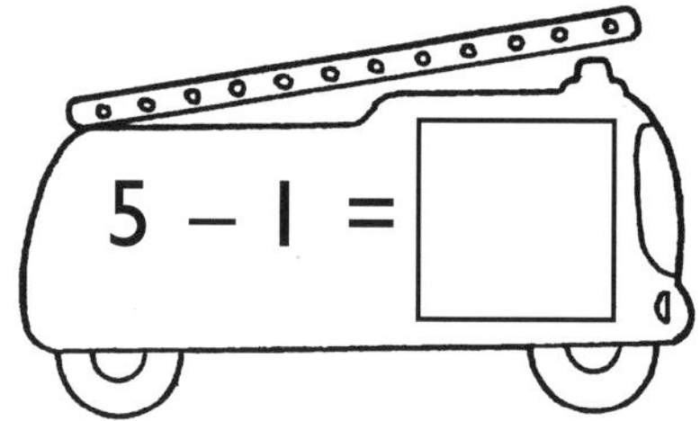

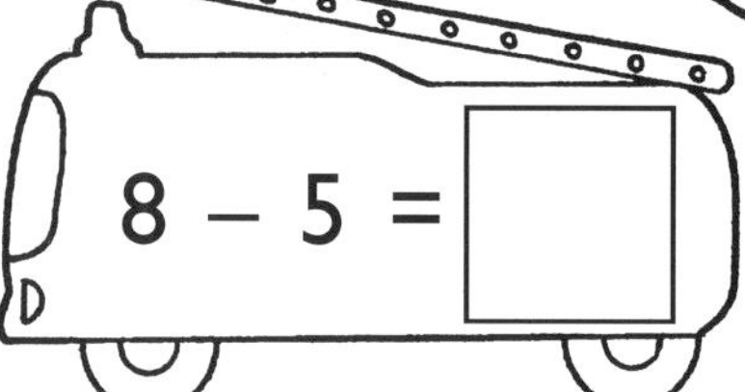

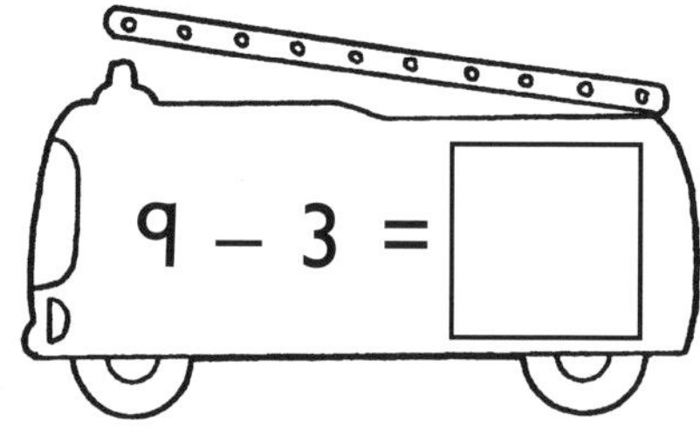

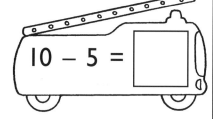

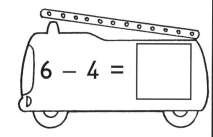

10 – 5 =

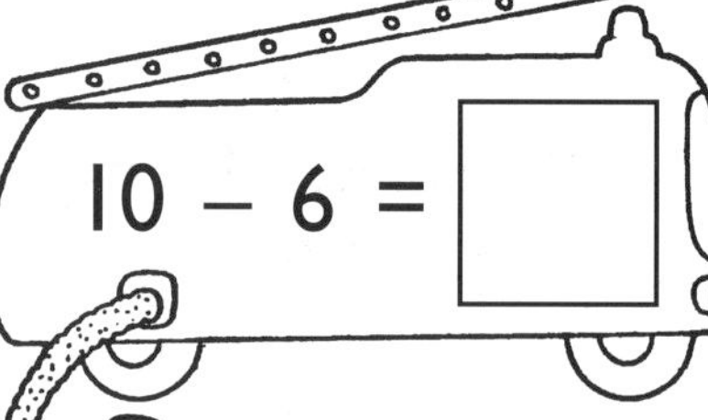

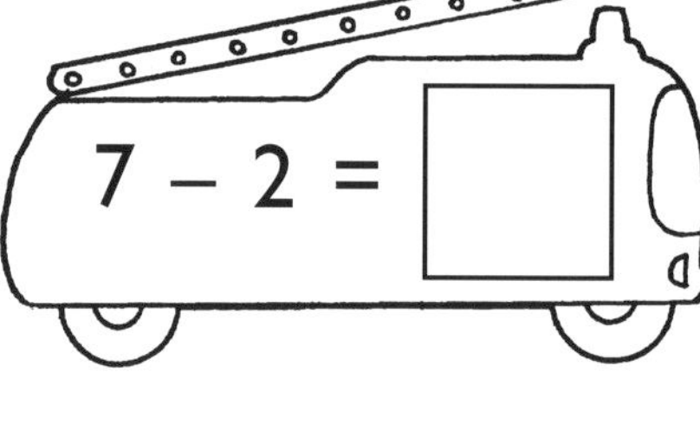

6 – 4 =

- **Write a subtraction on each fire engine.**

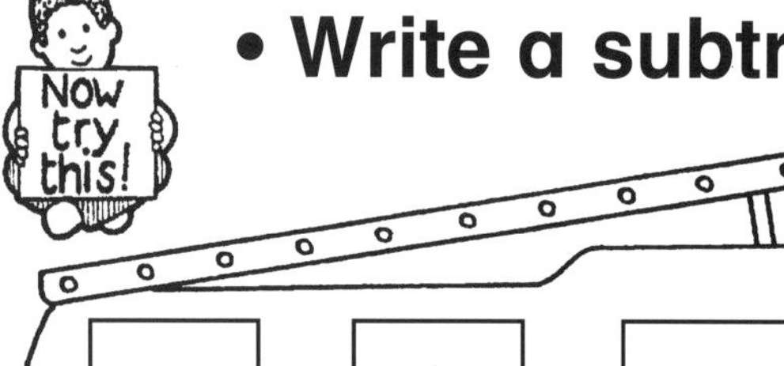

even answer

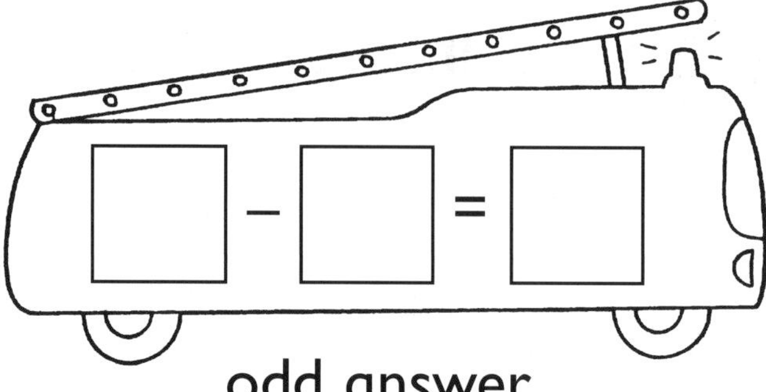

odd answer

Teachers' note If necessary, revise odd and even numbers. Note that zero is neither odd nor even. You could demonstrate practically to the children that even numbers of objects can always be arranged in twos, but with odd numbers there is always one left over. For the extension activity, children could be encouraged to use numbers greater than ten.

Next door numbers

The difference **between the numbers in each row is** 2 **.**

Subtract the numbers to find the difference.

• Write the numbers.

• Make the difference between next door numbers 3 **.**

Teachers' note In this activity, the children create sequences with a difference of two between the numbers. Ensure that the children understand how to work out the difference between two numbers.

Subtraction sentences

Use 9, 1 and 10 to make different number sentences.	Use 5, 2 and 7 to make different number sentences.
Use 6, 3 and 9 to make different number sentences.	Use 8, 2 and 10 to make different number sentences.
Use 4, 2 and 6 to make different number sentences.	Use 6, 2 and 8 to make different number sentences.

1	2	3	4	5	6	7
8	9	10	5	0	minus	

take away	less than	the same as	=
leaves	equals	from	–
and	is	take	the difference between

Teachers' note Provide one copy of the sheet for each pair of children to cut out the cards. In pairs, the children should choose an instruction card and make as many different number sentences as they can using the same set of three numbers. They may need to sort the cards first to match words with similar meanings. See page 20 for further instruction cards.

Little Bo Peep

- **Write the missing signs.**

Use + and –.

3 [+] 5 = 8

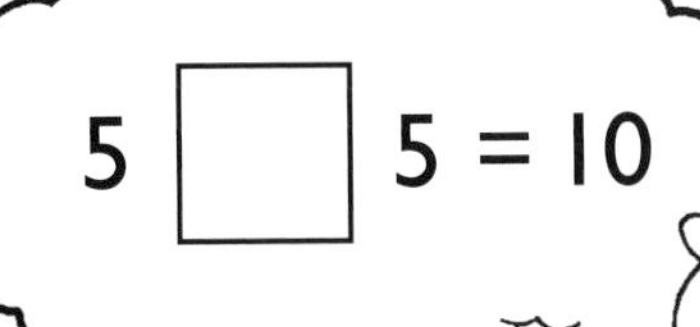

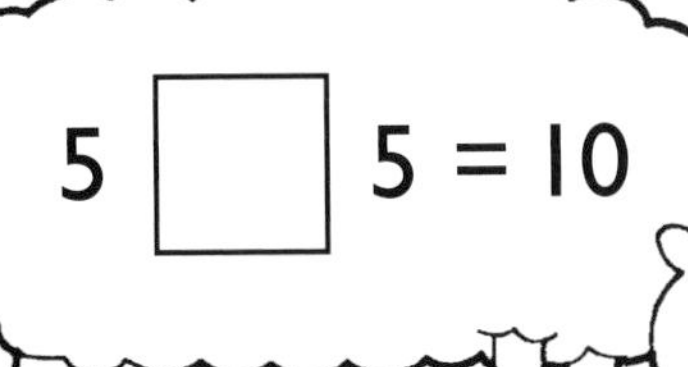

5 [ ] 5 = 10

8 [ ] 7 = 1

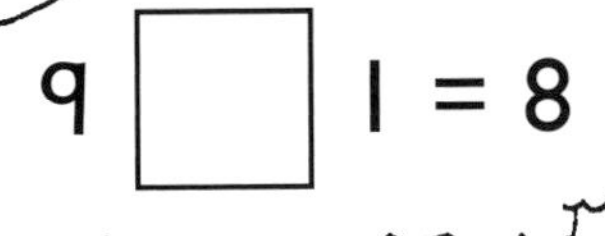

9 [ ] 1 = 8

5 [ ] 2 = 7

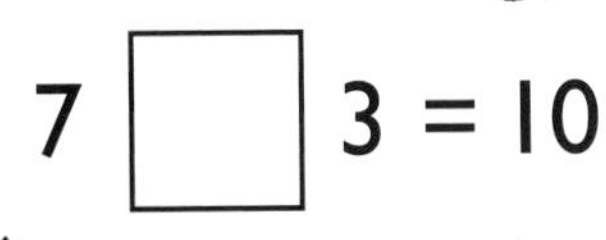

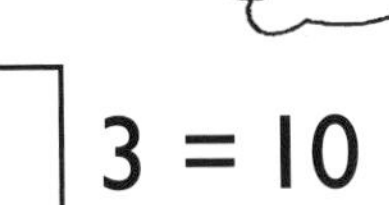

7 [ ] 3 = 10

8 [ ] 3 = 5

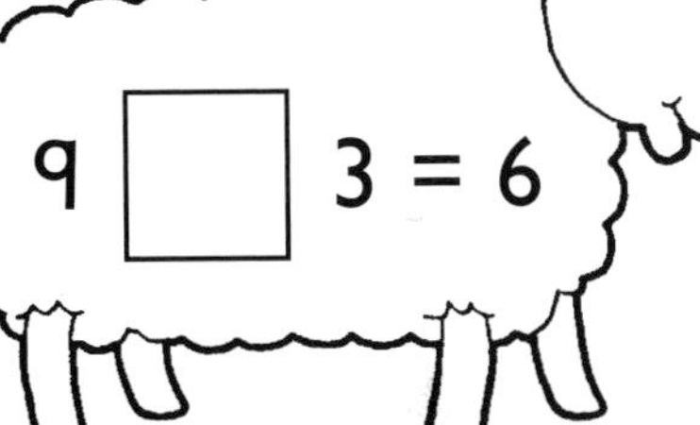

9 [ ] 3 = 6

6 [ ] 4 = 10

7 [ ] 2 = 5

- **Write the missing signs.**

5 [ ] 1 [ ] 2 = 4

Teachers' note Remind the children of the difference between plus and minus. Before starting, practise some questions of this kind on the board by writing number sentences and covering up the signs. As a further extension, the children could make up simple chain calculations such as 4 + 5 – 2 = 7. They then cover up the signs and ask a partner what they could be.

On the see-saw

- **Make each see-saw balance.**
- **Write the missing numbers.**

Now try this!

- **Make the see-saw balance. Write numbers in the boxes.**

7 – 3 = ☐ + ☐

Teachers' note Some children may need to use number lines. To introduce the activity, you could play 'What is the question' (see page 5). Demonstrate to the children using cubes that if the totals on each side of the see-saw are different, the see-saw will not balance. As a further extension, the children could draw their own see-saws and write balancing sums.

Mystery words

- Write the answers as words.
- Read down the grid to find the mystery word.

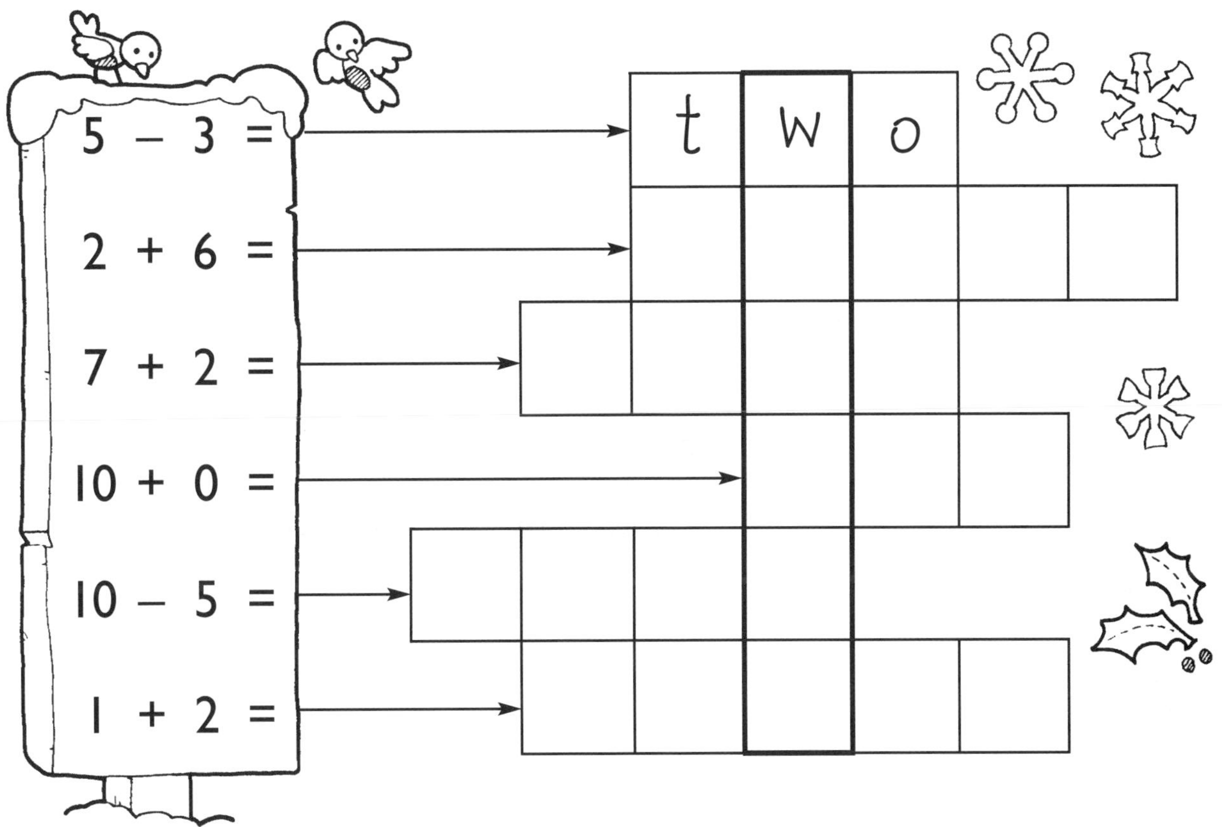

The mystery word is ______________________.

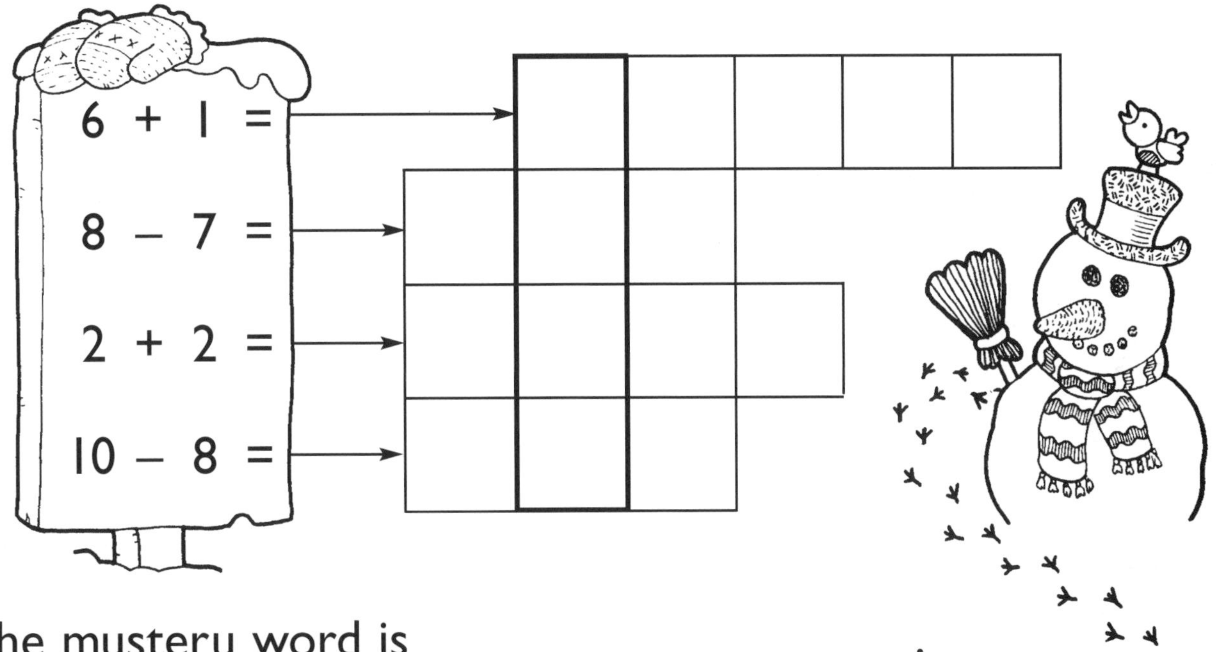

The mystery word is ______________________.

Teachers' note If necessary, display the number words one to ten for reference. Remind the children to write one letter in each square. For some children, the mystery word could be inserted and everything else left blank. The children can then work out the number word and write a sum to match it.

The garden path

- **Finish the number sentences.**
- **Use the number path and a counter to help you.**

Put the counter on **3**.

Count on 4.

Where do you land?

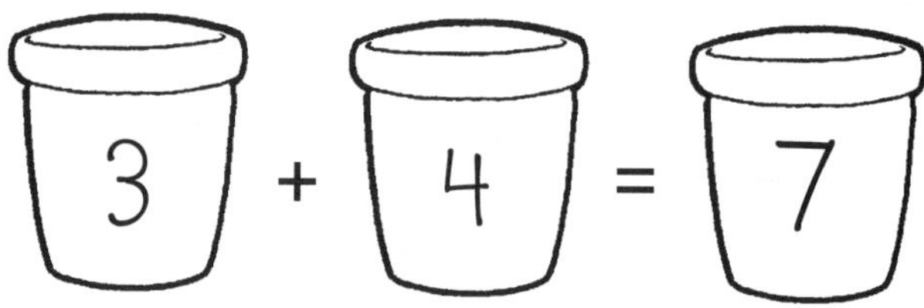

Put the counter on **7**.

Count back 5.

Where do you land?

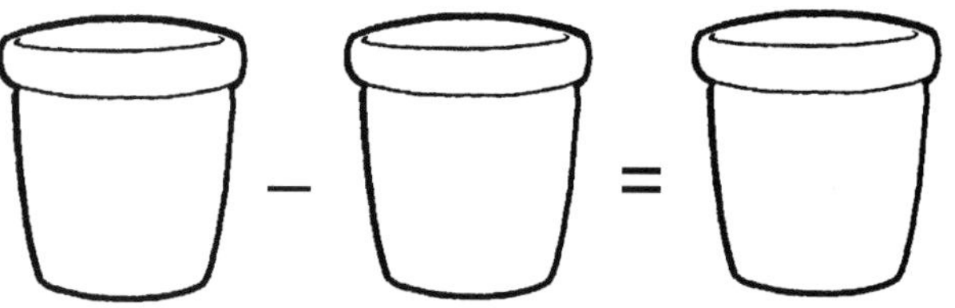

Put the counter on **6**.

Count back 6.

Where do you land?

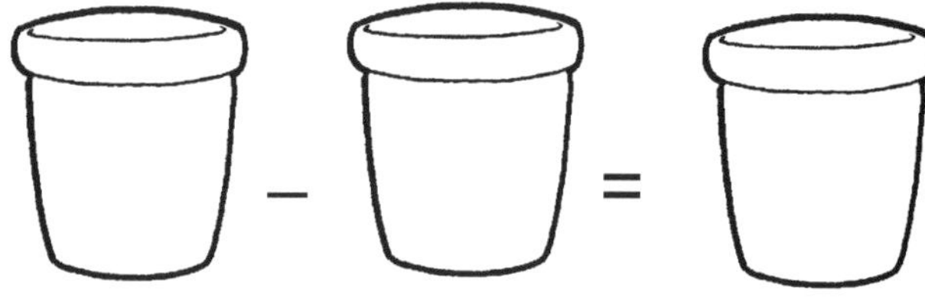

Put the counter on **2**.

Count on 7.

Where do you land?

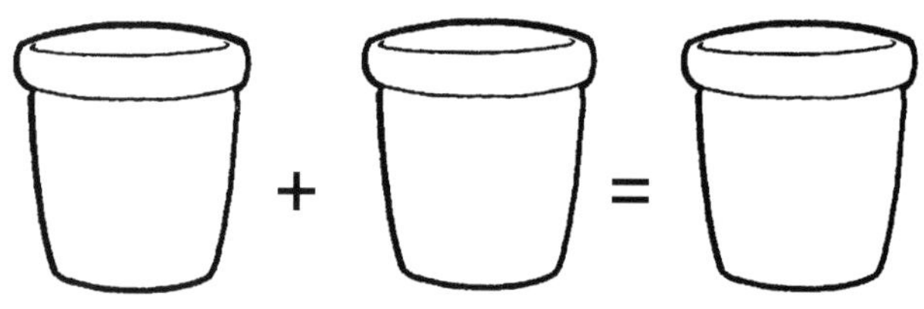

- **Write the missing numbers.**

5 +  = 9

 – 1 = 8

4 +  = 8

 – 5 = 5

 = 3

 +  = 8

Teachers' note Some children may need to use the number path to help with the extension activity. Discuss with the children how they worked out the answers and check which number facts they know by heart.

Paint splashes

Susie has splashed the paint pots!

- **Write the hidden numbers on the splashes.**

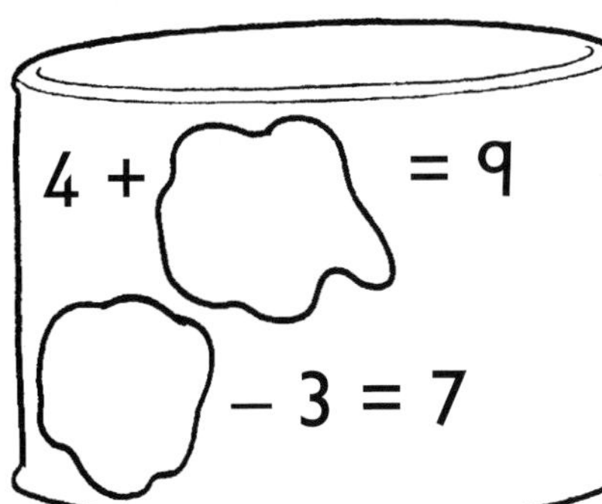

4 + = 8

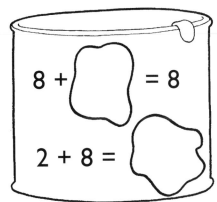

8 – 5 =

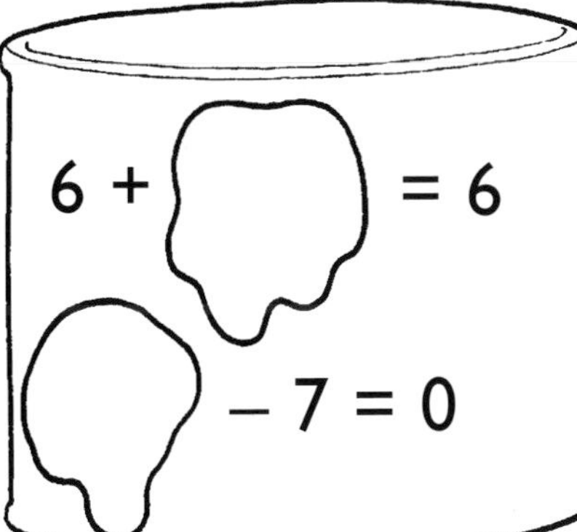

8 + = 8

2 + 8 =

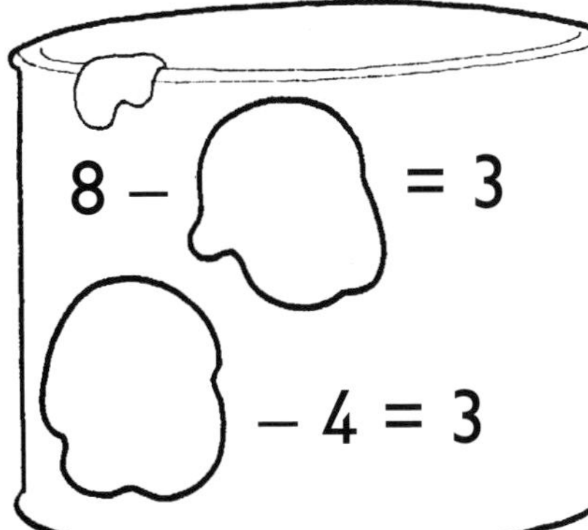

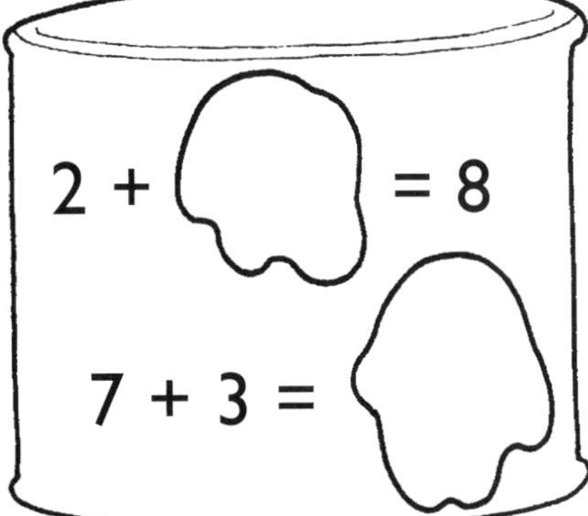

- **Write 3 number sentences to match each answer.** 5 7 8 4

Example: 4 + 1 = 5 7 – 2 = 5 10 – 5 = 5

Teachers' note Some children may need to use number lines or number tracks. Discuss with the children how they worked out the missing numbers. For the extension activity, some children could be encouraged to try chain calculations such as 2 + 6 – 3 = 5.

Treasure island game

• Play with a friend.

☆ Take turns to roll a dice.

☆ Move your counter.

☆ Say the answer. If you are right, collect a jewel.

The winner is the player with the most jewels.

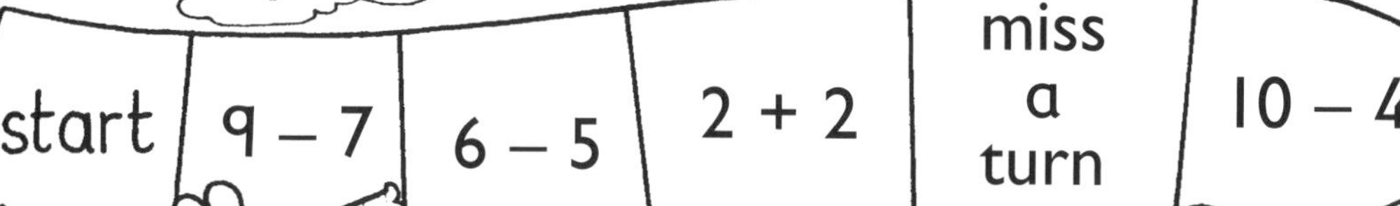

Teachers' note Each pair of children needs one copy of the sheet, a dice, two counters in different colours and objects to represent jewels (such as marbles, cubes, coins or sweets). Encourage the children to work out together whether or not the answer is correct.

Traffic jams

- **Cut out the labels at the bottom of the page.**
- **Write the missing words and numbers. Use the numbers [1] to [10].**

6	add	4	equals	
10	take away	2		
7			leaves	2
5			totals	8
8		3		5

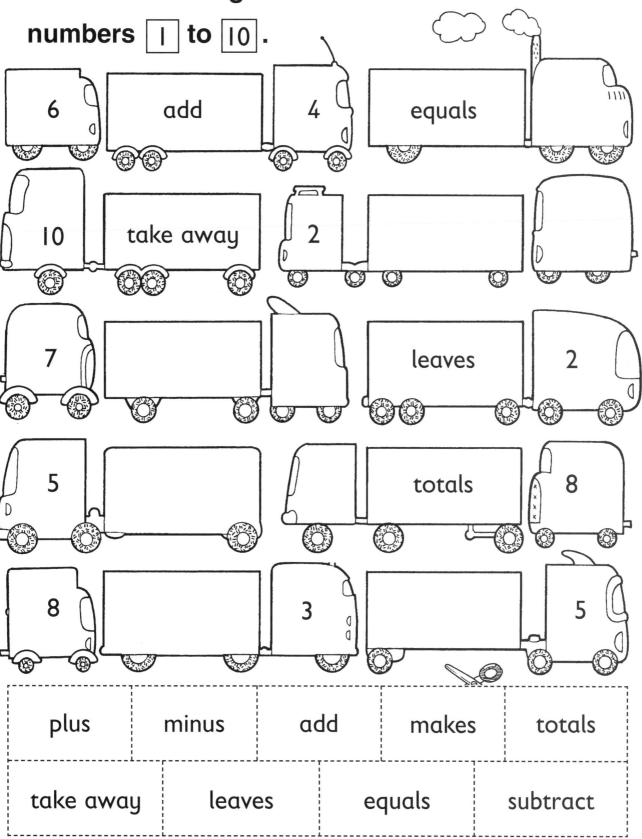

plus	minus	add	makes	totals
take away	leaves	equals	subtract	

Teachers' note It is important that children are able to use a variety of vocabulary for addition and subtraction. They should work in pairs or small groups to find several solutions to each problem and discuss the alternatives. Children can place the labels on the lorries before writing the answers. For the last problem, explain that the answer need not be on the right-hand side.

Number sentences

Use 7, 3 and 10 to make different number sentences.

7	is	3	less than	10
7	add	3	equals	10

1	2	3	4	5	6	7
8	9	10	5	0	add	
take	is	and	+	–	=	
plus	more than	the same as				
makes	totals	altogether				
minus	less than	take away				
leaves	equals	the same as				
the difference between	from					

Teachers' note Provide one copy of the sheet for each pair of children to cut out the cards. In pairs, the children should read the instruction card and make as many different number sentences as they can. They may need to sort the cards first to match words with similar meanings. They can repeat using another set of three numbers (see pages 20 and 32).

Playful kittens

- **Write the answers.**
- **Join each bowl to the correct cat.**

0 5 10 15 20

5 + 7 = 12

8 + 3 =

8 + 8 =

5 + 8 =

6 + 7 =

4 + 8 =

- **Write the answers on the cat flaps.**

9 + 5 = 14

5 + 6 =

2 + 9 =

3 + 8 =

7 + 7 =

8 + 7 =

- **Write your own additions.**

Make the answers even.

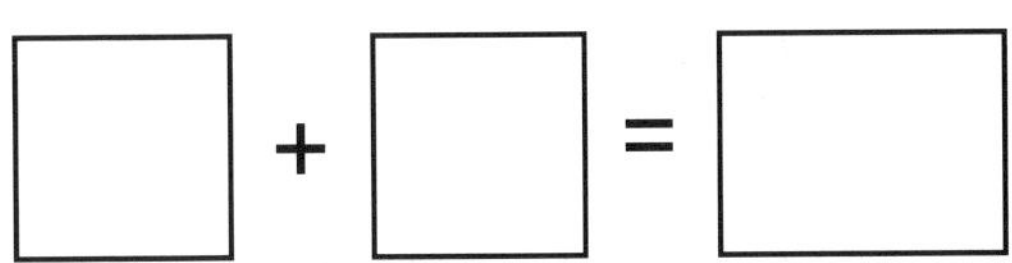

☐ + ☐ = ☐ ☐ + ☐ = ☐

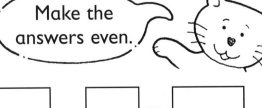

Teachers' note With the whole class, talk about the 'missing' numbers on the number line. Discuss how the answers can be worked out and remind the children that counting on from the larger number is a quick way of adding. Explain that the order of adding does not matter (for example, 4 + 8 has the same answer as 8 + 4).

Sweet treats

You can write 11 as tens and ones, like this.

11 = 10 + 1

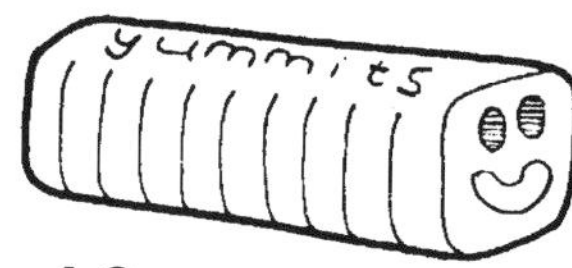

11 yummits = 10 yummits + 1 yummit

- Write the missing numbers.

10 = 10 + 0   11 = 10 + 1   12 = 10 + ☐

13 = 10 + ☐   14 = 10 + ☐   15 = 10 + ☐

16 = 10 + ☐   17 = 10 + ☐   18 = 10 + ☐

19 = 10 + ☐

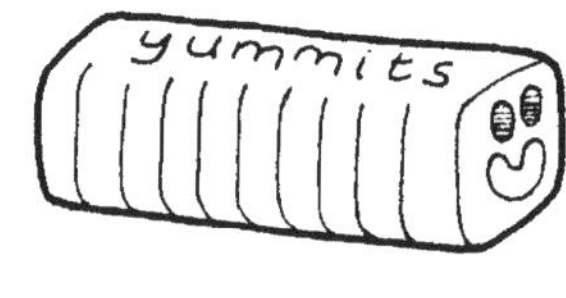

- Write the missing numbers.

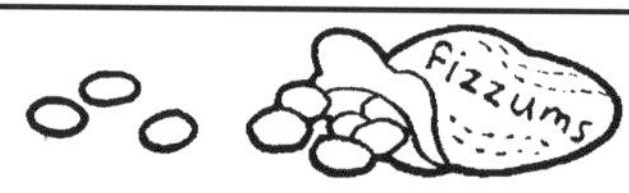

10 + ☐ = 16   ☐ + 3 = 13   10 + ☐ = 19

15 = ☐ + 5   10 + ☐ = 12   ☐ + 8 = 18

- Choose 4 numbers to put in the machine.
- Write the number sentences.

2 + 10 = 12

______________   ______________

____

Teachers' note Ensure that the children understand the tens and ones structure for the numbers 10 to 19. Encourage them to practise adding 10 to single numbers. Some children may be able to add 10 to numbers greater than 10.

Sea creatures

- **Add 0 to these numbers.**

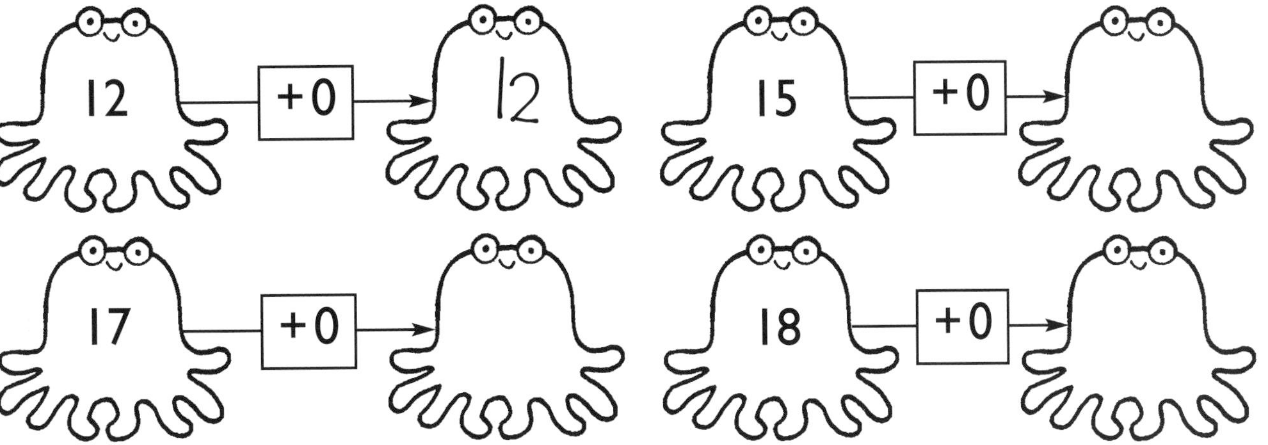

- **Add 1 to these numbers.**

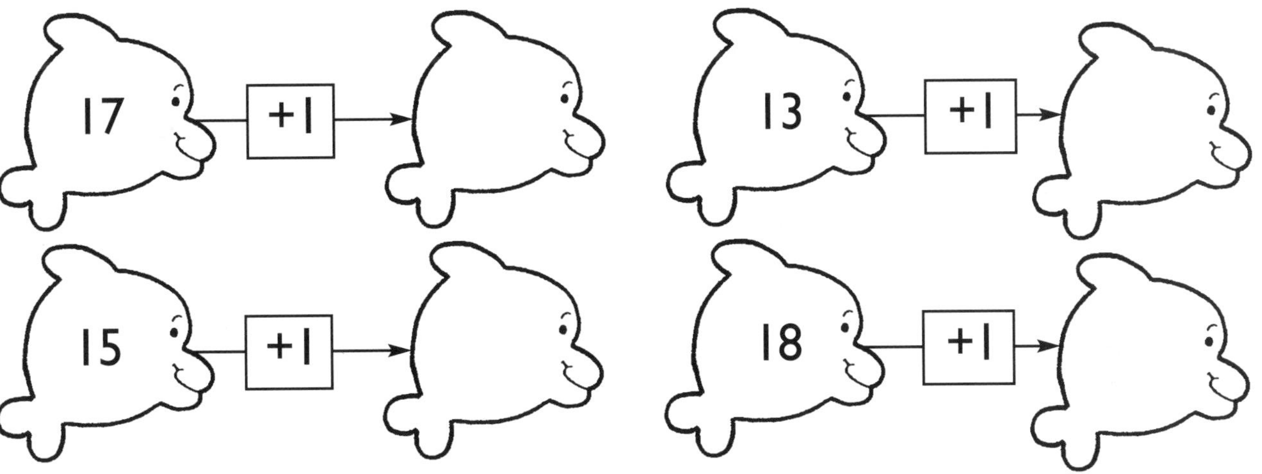

- **Add 10 to these numbers.**

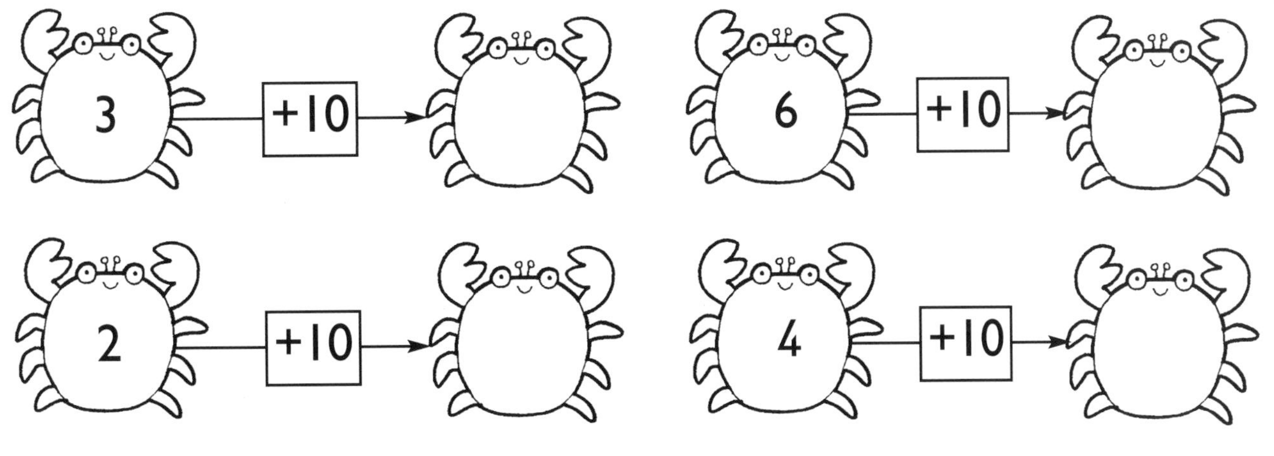

Teachers' note This activity provides practice in quickly adding 0, 1 and 10 to a range of numbers. You could introduce this by playing 'Unison response' (see page 5). The children should work out the answers fairly rapidly. Some children may be able to work with numbers greater than 20. The page could also be adapted to practise adding 9.

Parachutes

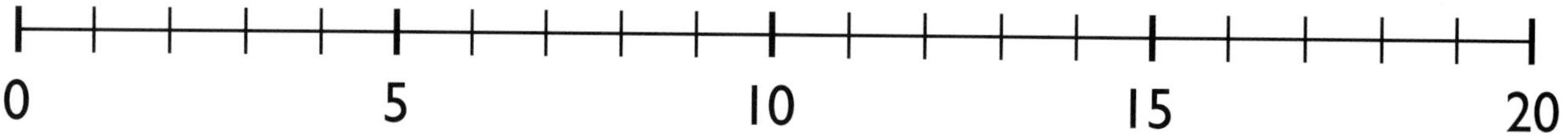

- **Each person is carrying 20 gold bars.**
- **Write the missing numbers to total 20.**

- **Make each balloon total 21.**

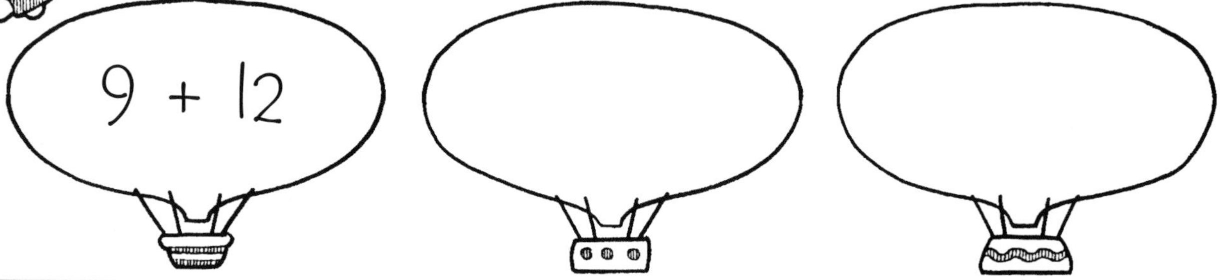

Teachers' note With the whole class, talk about the 'missing' numbers on the number line. Discuss how the answers can be worked out and remind the children that counting on from the larger number is a quick way of adding. Explain that the order of adding does not matter (for example, 7 + 13 has the same answer as 13 + 7).

House puzzle

- **Write the answers as words.**
- **Read down the grids to find the house number.**

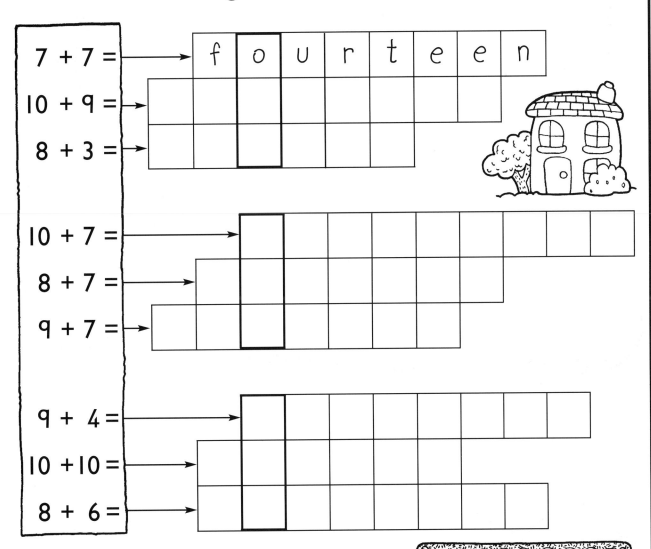

7 + 7 = f o u r t e e n

10 + 9 =

8 + 3 =

10 + 7 =

8 + 7 =

9 + 7 =

9 + 4 =

10 + 10 =

8 + 6 =

- **Write each number in figures.** ___ ___ ___

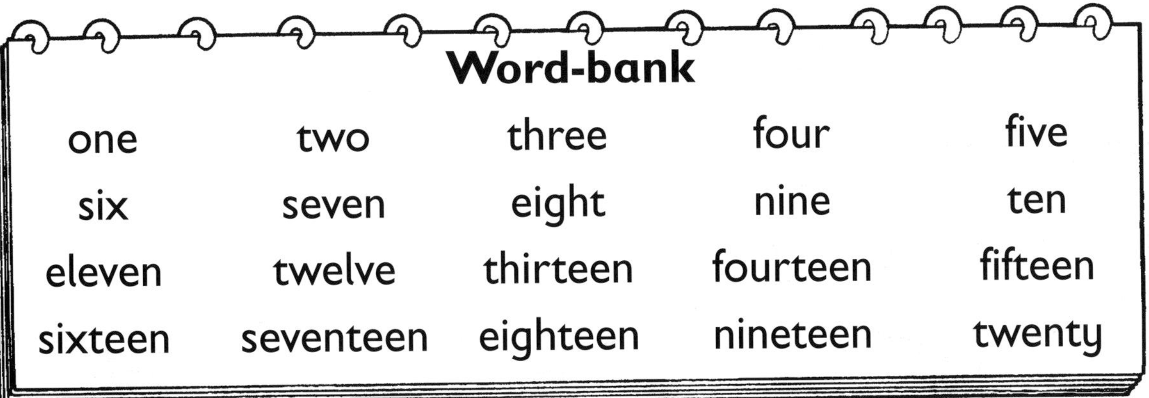

Word-bank
one
two
three
four
five
six
seven
eight
nine
ten
eleven
twelve
thirteen
fourteen
fifteen
sixteen
seventeen
eighteen
nineteen
twenty

Teachers' note Provide number lines for any children who need counting aids. If appropriate, you could mask the word-bank at the bottom of the page.

Window totals

0					5					10					15					20

- **Ring pairs of next door numbers that total 13.**

5	7	6	9
7	2	3	4
3	10	8	5
4	10	6	6

- **Write the number pairs.**

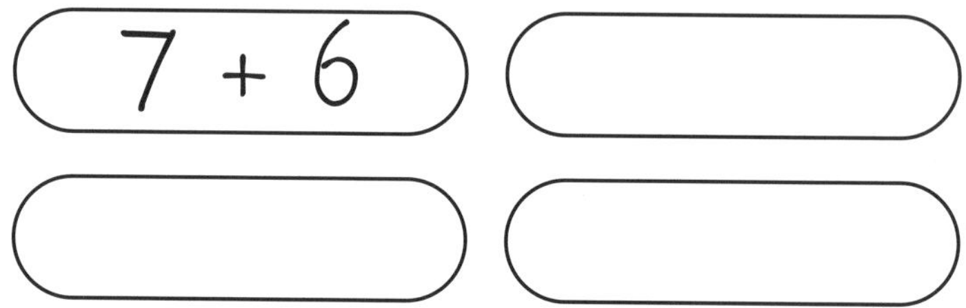

- **Ring pairs of next door numbers that total 12.**

6	3	9	4
1	2	10	8
6	6	5	7
3	10	9	2

- **Write the number pairs.**

Now try this!

- **Write pairs of numbers that total 14.**

Teachers' note Explain to the children that pairs of numbers in the grid must be touching each other horizontally or vertically. If children use the number line, ensure that they count on from the larger number and that they count hops along the line to match the counting on number. Some children may start to remember some of the number facts, particularly the doubles.

Adding 9

- **To add 9, you can add 10, then take away 1.**

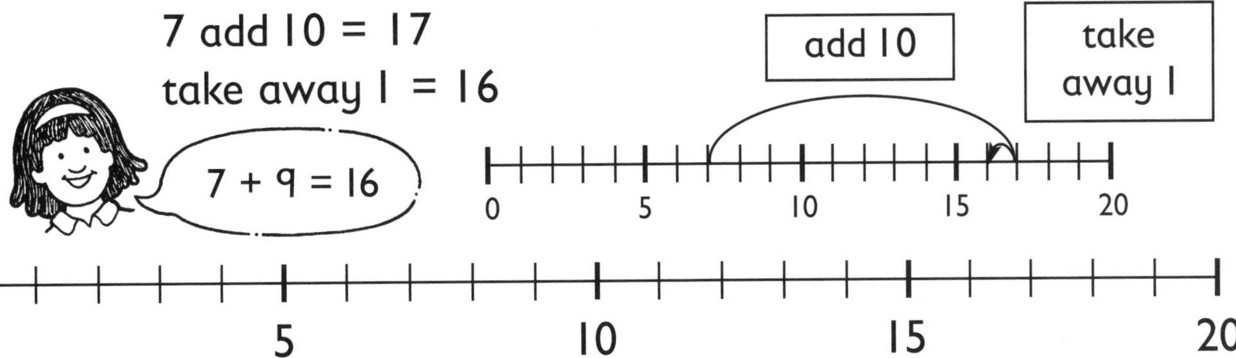

0 5 10 15 20

- **Use the number line to help you add 9.**

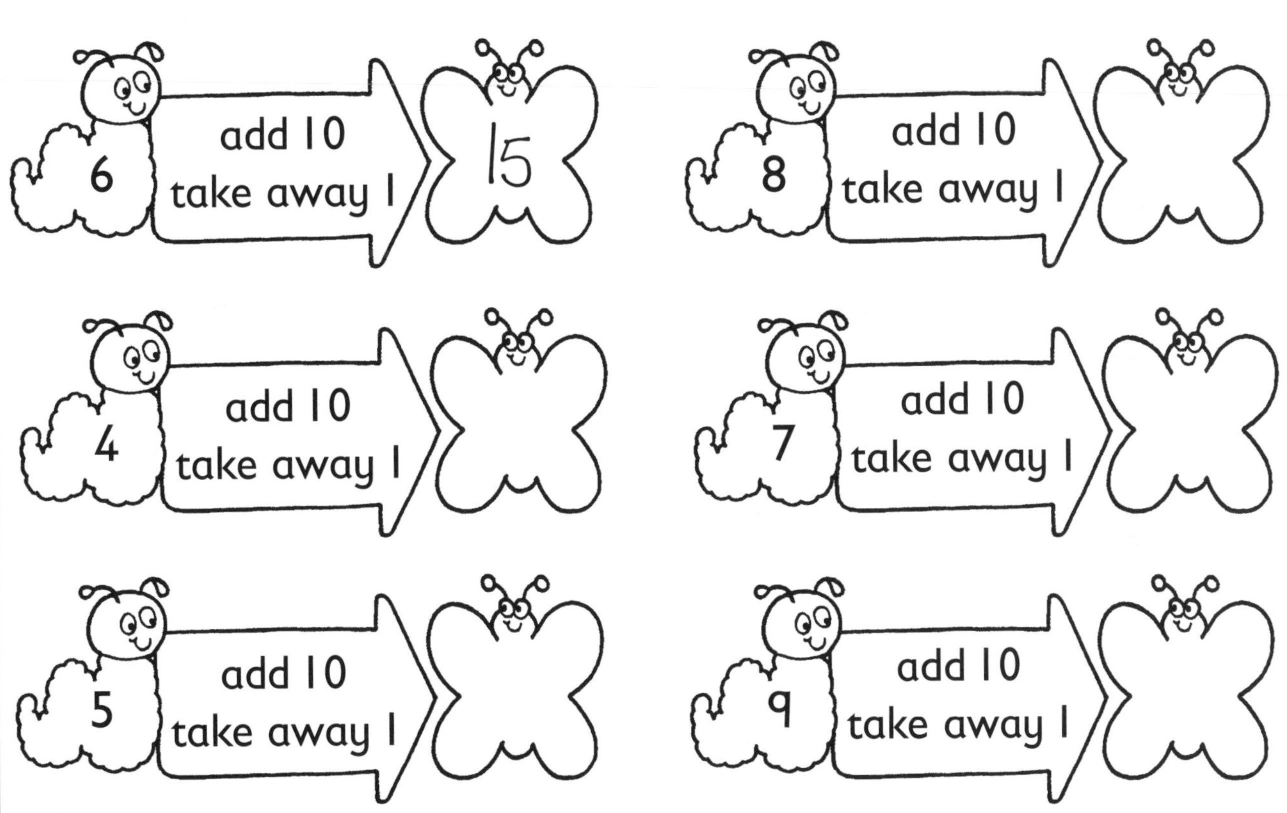

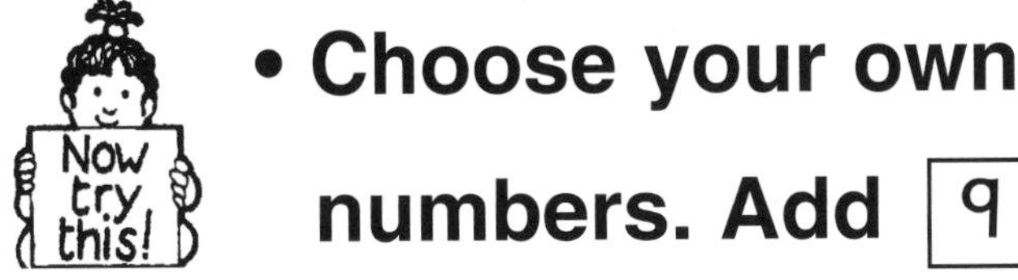

- **Choose your own numbers. Add 9.**

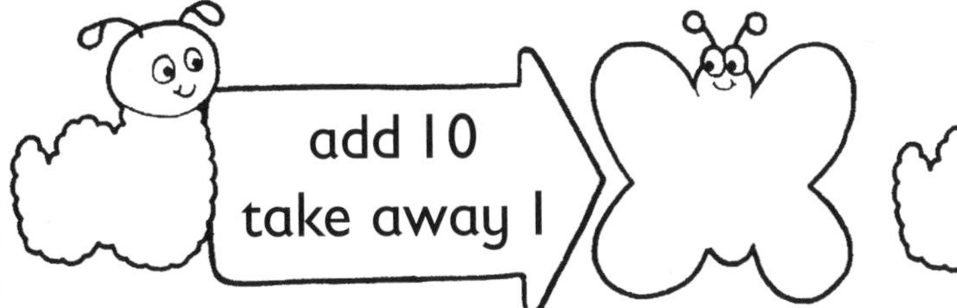

Teachers' note Before beginning the activity, introduce this quick method of adding nine and ensure that the children understand the process. Provide copies of the 100-grid on page 63 for the children to use in the extension activity.

Purse totals

- **Write the total in each purse.**

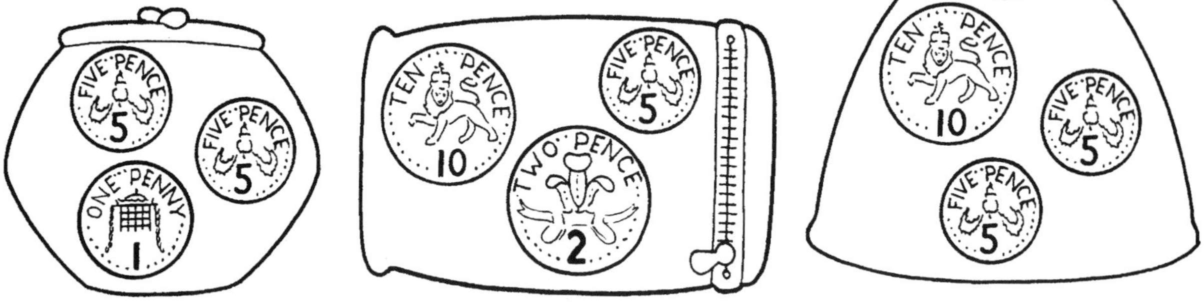

11 p	p	p
p	p	p

- **Write the total cost.**

6p 8p | 9p 5p sizzlers | 13p munchy bar 3p

p	p	p

Now try this!

- **Write labels that total 20p.**

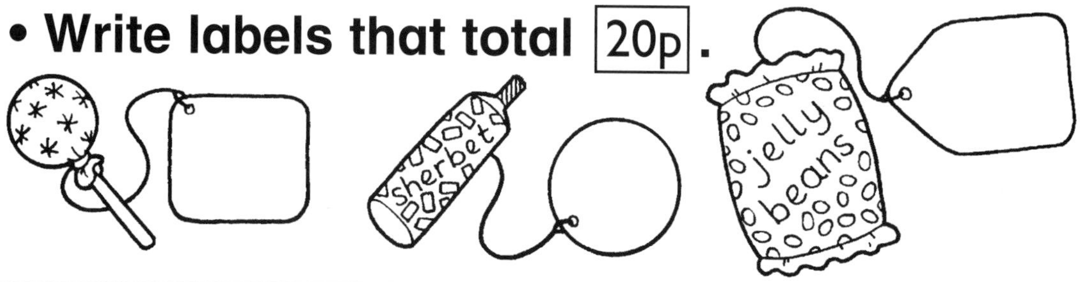

sherbet | jelly beans

Teachers' note Discuss which strategies the children use, and challenge them to manage without a number line. Encourage mental methods of addition, such as counting on from the coin of the highest value. The children could explore different ways of making a value such as 20p. They can investigate totals to 20p, including which totals can be made with three coins and which cannot.

Relay race

• Write the numbers on the relay runners.

Teachers' note Make sure the children know that when they subtract, the numbers become smaller. Provide number lines if necessary; check that the children count the number of jumps along the line. As an extension, ask them to colour all the even (or odd) numbers in each relay race. You could use the 100-track on page 64 for further counting back activities.

Flying high

- Join each kite to the answer on the number line.

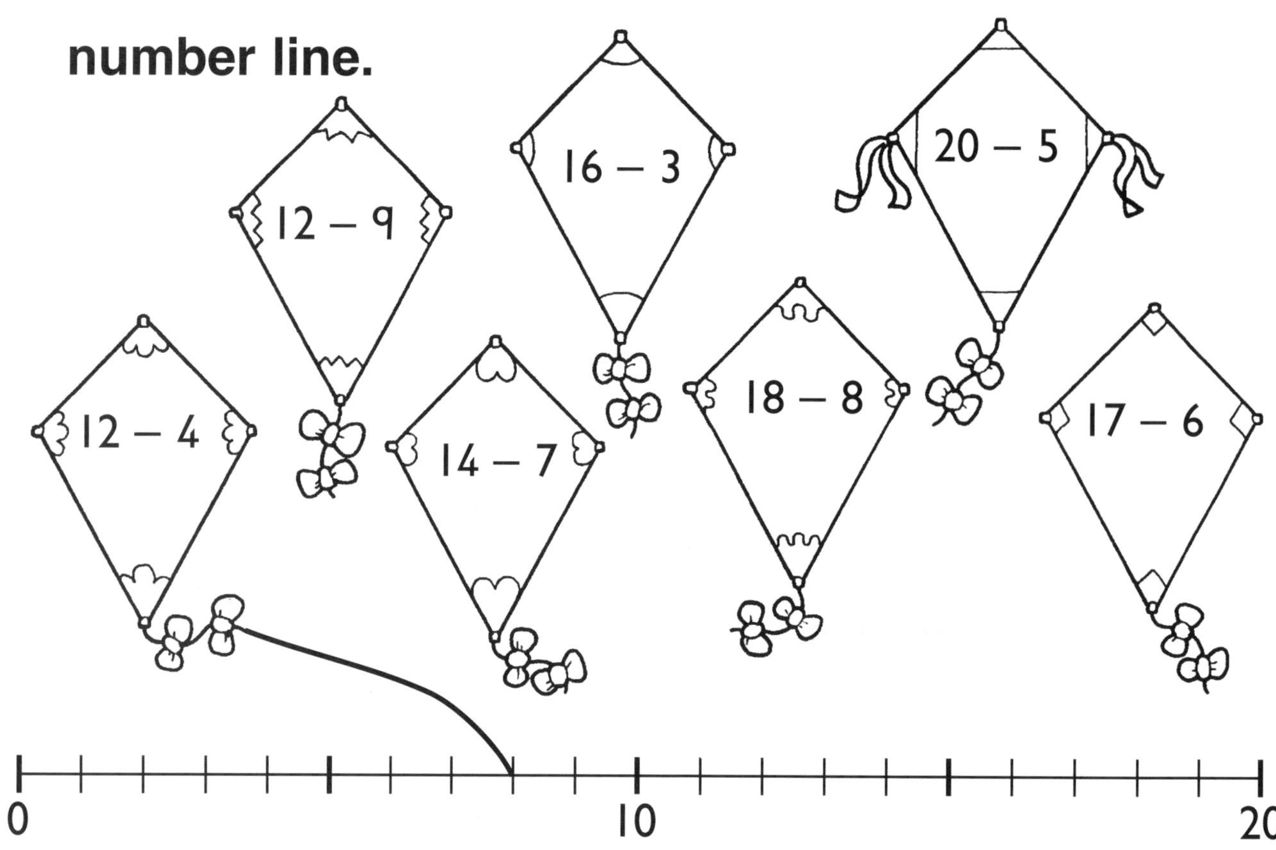

- Finish the subtractions to match the answer on the sun.

- Write subtractions to match the answer on the sun.

Teachers' note Make sure the children know that when they subtract, the numbers become smaller. Check that they count the number of jumps when subtracting on a number line. For the extension activity, you could explain to the children that they are finding numbers which have a difference of four. The 100-track on page 64 can be used for further counting back activities.

Superheroes

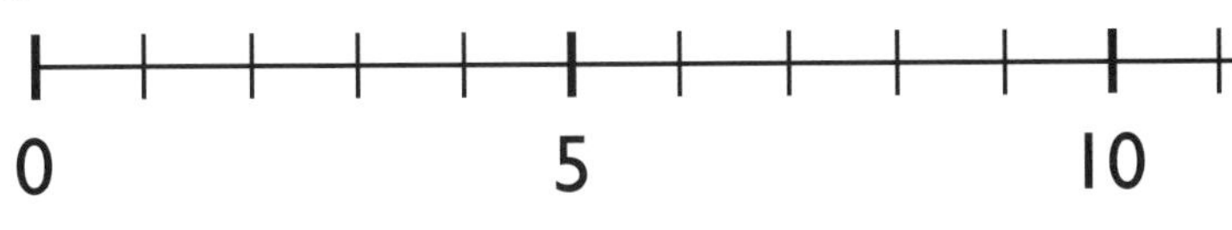

- **Look at the code wheel.**

- **Answer all the subtractions.**

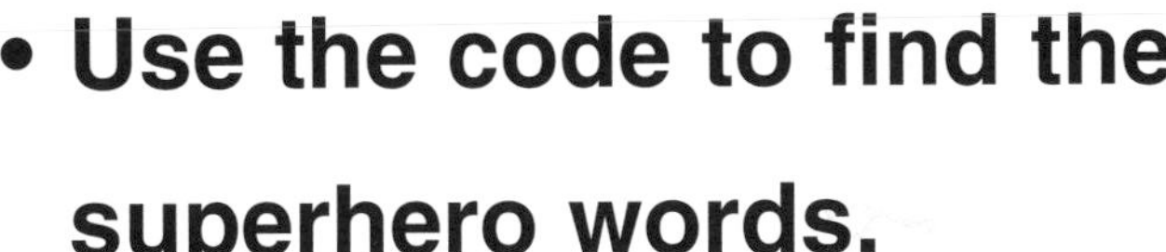

- **Use the code to find the superhero words.**

14–12	20–13	15–13
2		

p ___ ___

18–10	12–11	16–13	20–15

___ ___ ___ ___

19–15	16–15	13–11

___ ___ ___

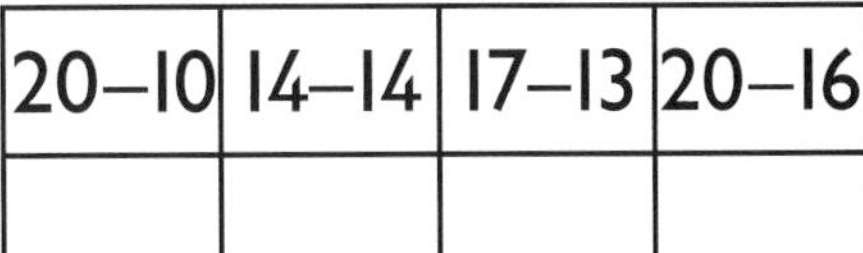

20–10	14–14	17–13	20–16

___ ___ ___ ___

Now try this!

- **Write number clues to spell out** whizz.

Example: w 20 – 11 = 9
h ...

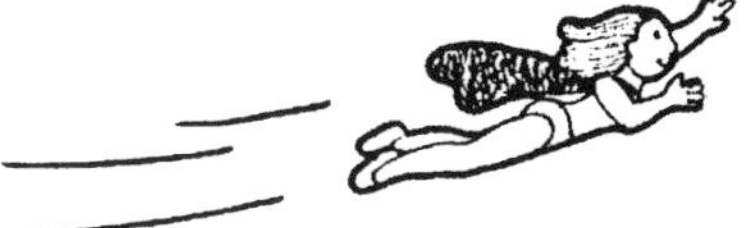

Teachers' note Discuss with the children strategies for working out subtractions of numbers which are quite close together. Encourage them to find the two numbers on the number line and count between them – this is often more efficient than finding the first and counting back by the second. Extend to using pairs of numbers on a 100-grid and 100-track (pages 63 and 64).

Spending money

• **Work out how much change from 20p.**

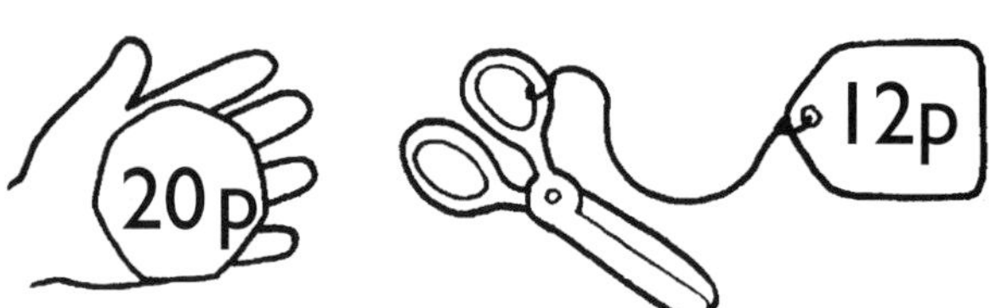

20p – 12 p = 8 p

15p

20p – ☐ p = ☐ p

20p – ☐ p = ☐ p

stickers

3p

20p – ☐ p = ☐ p

• **Write how much change.**

change = ☐ p

change = ☐ p

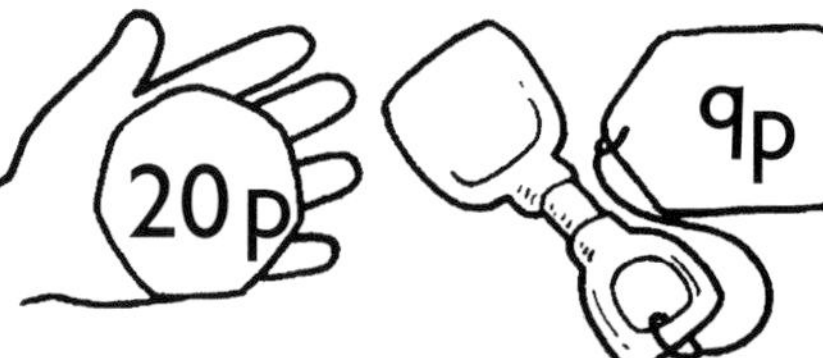

change = ☐ p

The coins show your change from 20p.

• **Write how much you spent.**

ONE PENNY 1

I spent ☐ p

I spent ☐ p

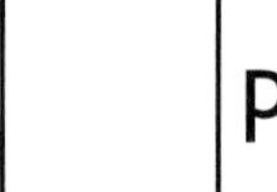

Teachers' note Ensure that the children are confident with changing 20p for equivalent amounts, and do not always change the 20p coin into twenty 1p coins. In pairs, children could play a game with a set of coins totalling 20p and a yoghurt pot. One child puts some of the coins under the pot and the other child works out how much is hidden. They swap roles and repeat.

Dotty puzzle

- **Write all the answers.**
- **Join the dots in the same order as the answers.**

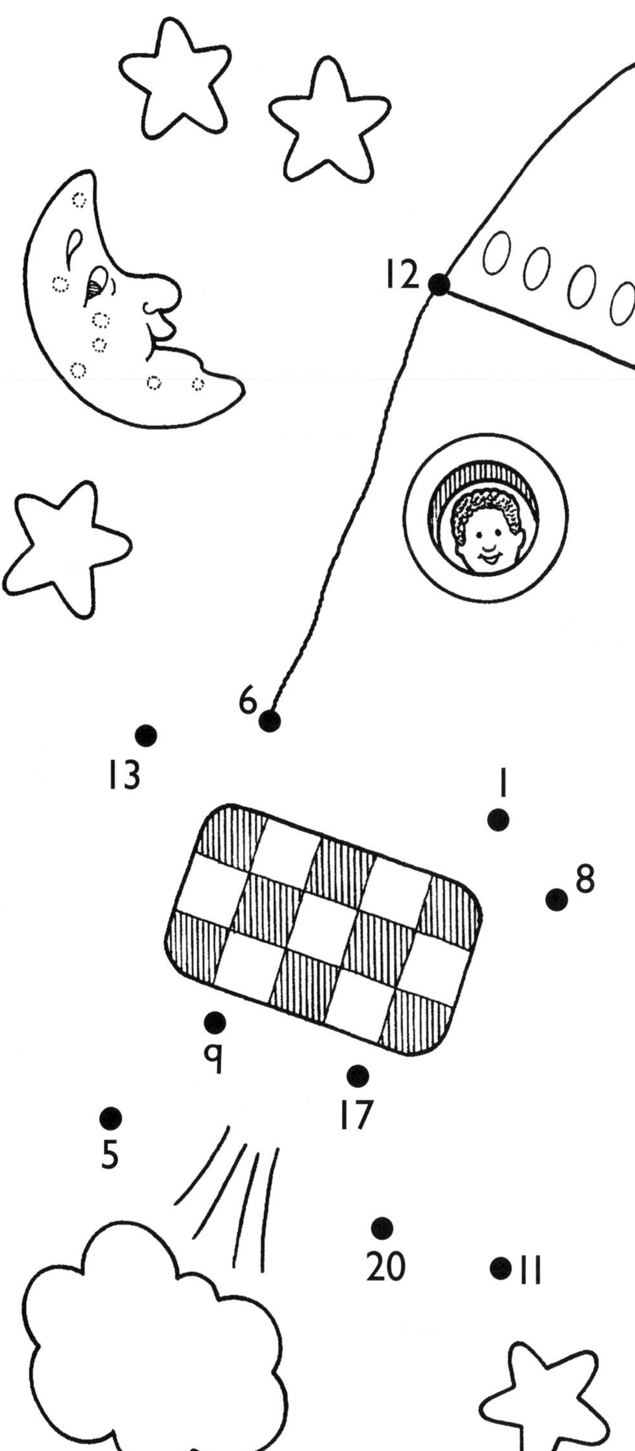

1. 10 + 2 = 12

2. 10 – 4 = 6

3. 10 + 3 =

4. 10 – 7 =

5. 10 – 5 =

6. 10 – 1 =

7. 10 + 7 =

8. 10 + 10 =

9. 10 + 1 =

10. 10 – 2 =

11. 10 – 9 =

12. 10 + 5 =

Teachers' note This activity provides practice in adding on 10 and subtracting from 10. Encourage the children to find the answers fairly rapidly; calculation aids should not be needed by the majority of children. Make sure the children understand that they are not joining the dots in numerical order (1, 2, 3…) but in answer order (12, 6, 13…).

Collecting shells

• Play with a friend.

☆ Take turns to roll 2 dice.

☆ Add the numbers together. $1 + 4 = 5$

☆ Subtract the total from **20**. $20 - 5 = 15$

☆ Colour your shell with that number.

☆ The winner is the first to colour 6 shells.

Name ____________	Name ____________
17, 11, 9, 13, 8, 18, 14, 10, 16, 12, 15	18, 13, 8, 12, 16, 15, 10, 17, 11, 9, 14

Teachers' note Each pair of children needs one copy of the sheet, two dice and coloured pencils. Some answers will occur several times (in theory, the most frequent answers will be 12, 13 and 14; the least frequent will be 8 and 18). If a child gets a number that has already been coloured in, the child misses that turn. The children could write down the number sentences.

Pet mix-up

Which pet belongs to which wizard?

• **Follow the instructions. Write the answer.**

10 11 12 13 14 15 16 17

Start at 13.
Count on 4.
Count back 1.

Pet number ☐

Start at 14.
Count back 2.
Count on 5.

Pet number ☐

Start at 12.
Count on 4.
Count back 5.
Count on 3.

Pet number ☐

Start at 16.
Count back 2.
Count back 4.
Count on 3.

Pet number ☐

• **Write numbers on the animals.**

• **Write a puzzle for a friend.**

Start at ____. Count back ___. Count on ___. Count back ___.

Animal number and name ______________________________

Teachers' note Encourage the children to use larger numbers in the extension activity. They should give their puzzle to a friend, who writes the animal number and name. The original child can then check whether the answer is right.

Buzzing bees

This is a double.

3 + 3 = 6

This is a near double.

3 + 4 = 7

- **Write these doubles.**

☐ + ☐ = 4

☐ + ☐ = ☐

☐ + ☐ = ☐

- **Write these near doubles.**

☐ + ☐ = 5

☐ + ☐ = ☐

☐ + ☐ = ☐

- **Draw the missing ants to match the total.**

total 5

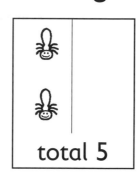

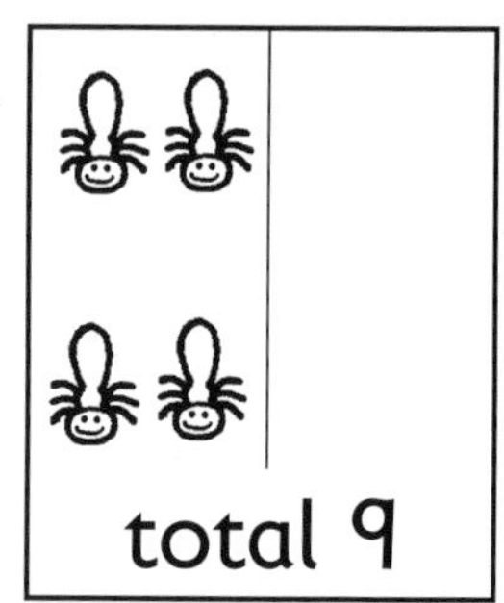

Teachers' note Introduce or revise doubles and near doubles. Ensure that the children can quickly double numbers between one and five. For the extension activity, you could ask the children to colour the doubles.

All at sea

- **Join each boat to the correct number on the lighthouse.**

- **Write which numbers have no boats.**

- **Complete the boats.**

Teachers' note Some children may need to use counting aids for this activity. You could suggest that they use different colour pencils for each line.

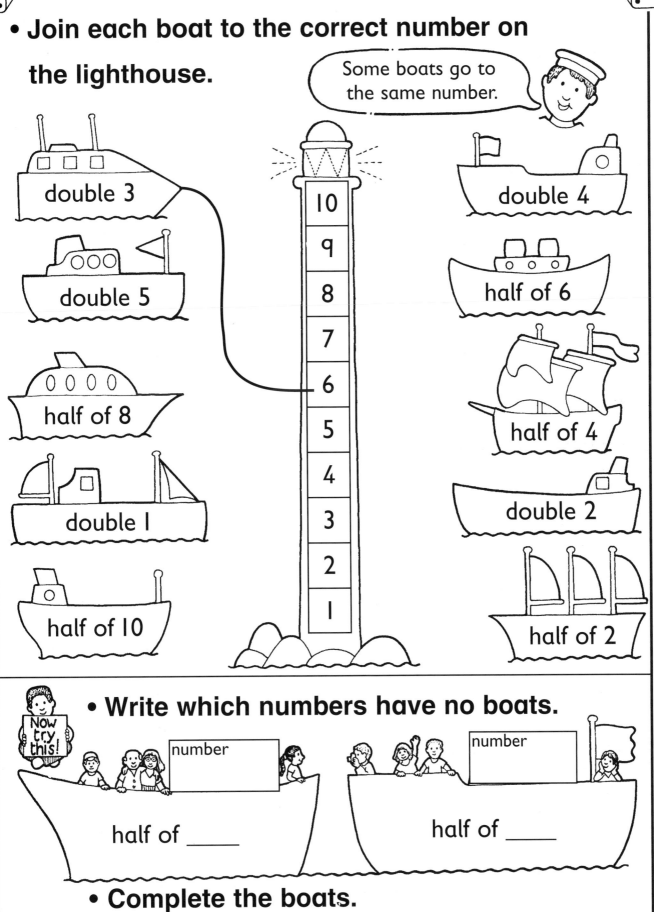

Double your money

- Double the amount in each money box.

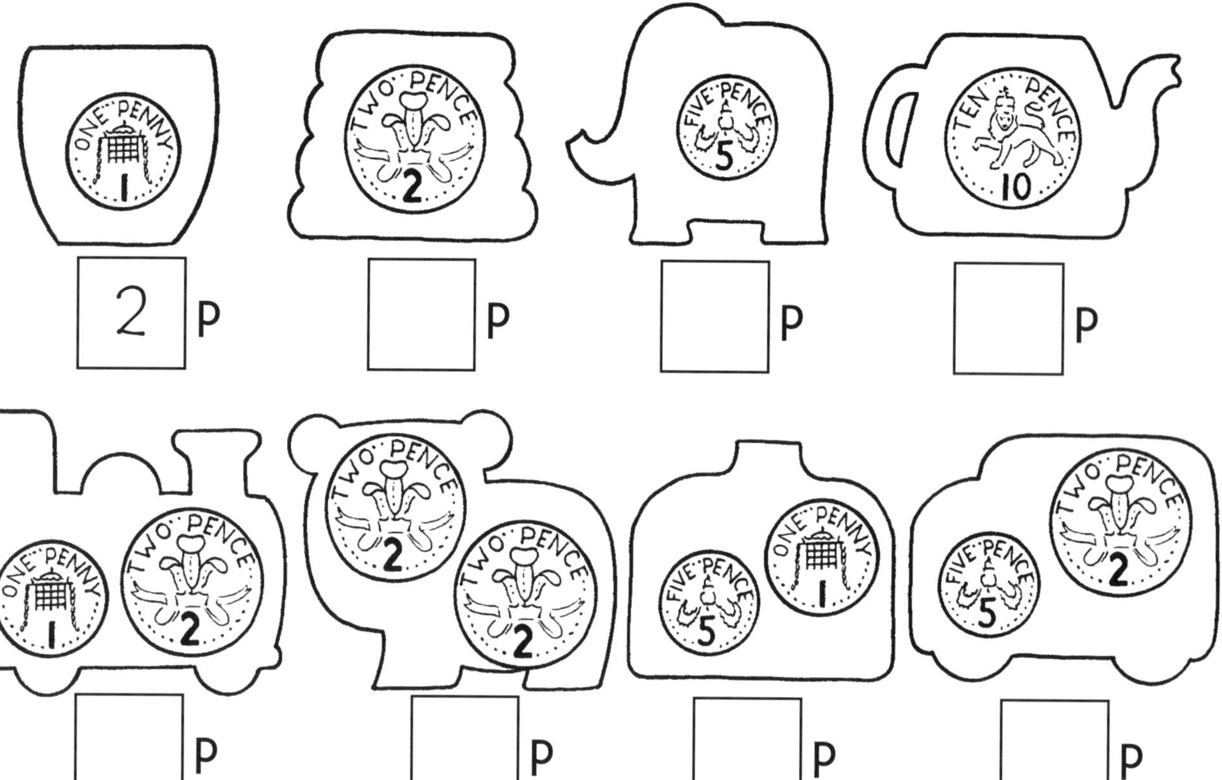

- Join money boxes which have the same total.

- Draw your own money box and coins.
- Ask a friend to double the amount.

Teachers' note If possible, provide real coins for the children to work with. Some children may find it helpful to use a 1–100 number line.

Party time

- **Write the missing numbers.**

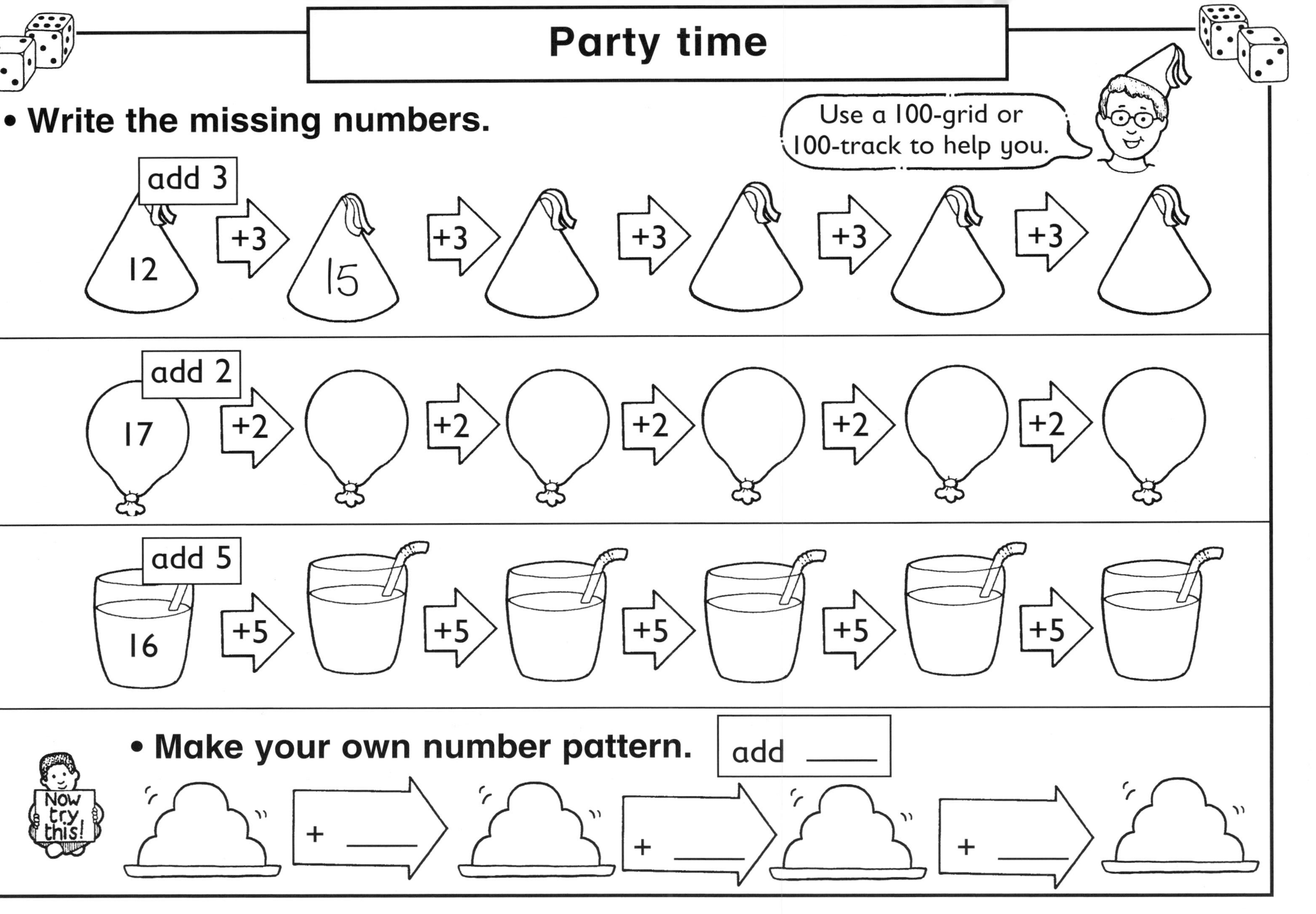

Teachers' note Provide copies of the 100-grid and 100-track on pages 63 and 64. Using both the grid and the track will help to reinforce the idea of counting on. Children can tap their heads as they say the start number (for reinforcement and to prevent them including it as part of the count), and then keep a tally on their fingers as they count on. See also the note on page 60.

Fun swim

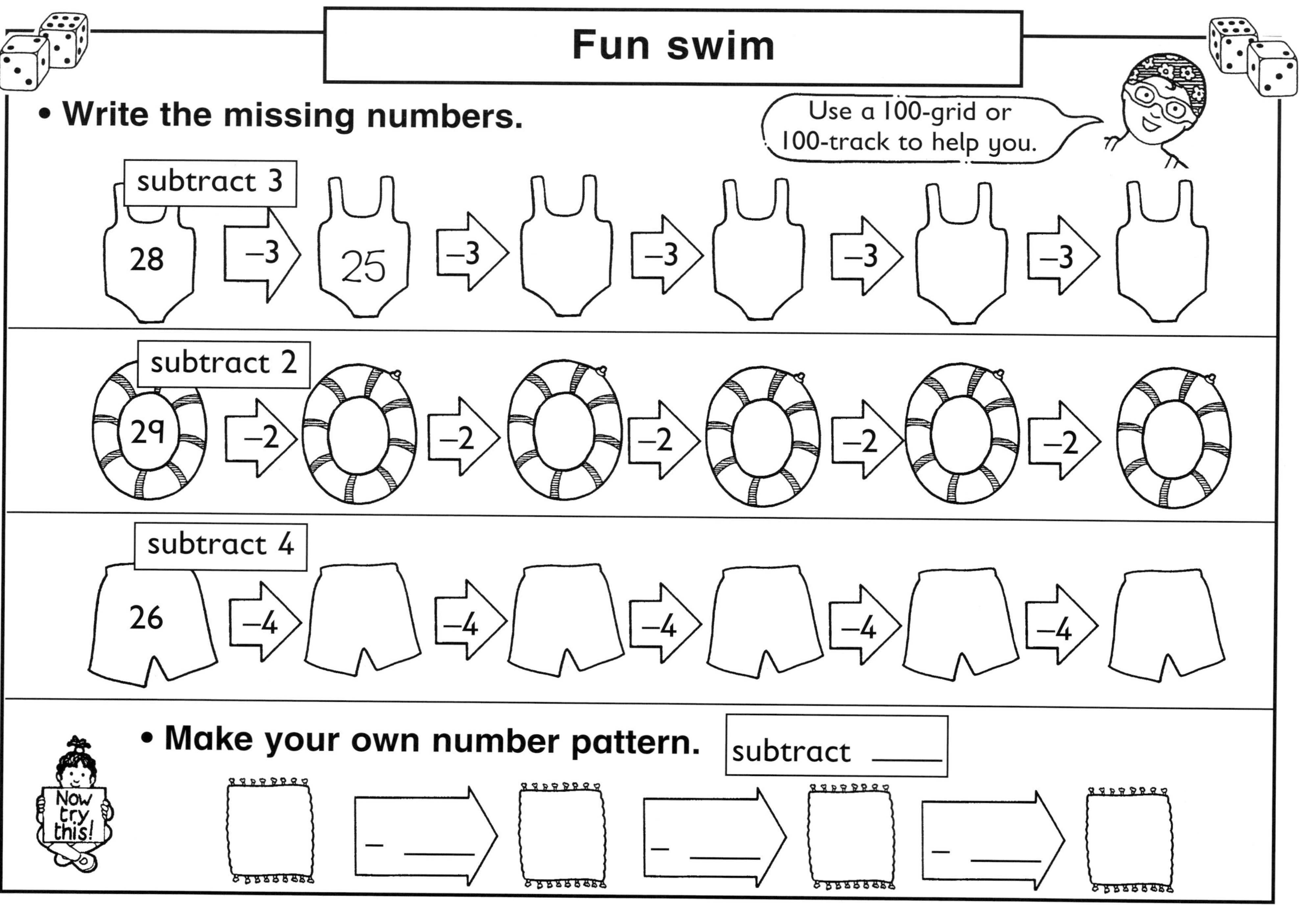

Teachers' note Provide copies of the 100-grid and 100-track on pages 63 and 64. As a further extension, you could insert a finish number and mask out all the other numbers on the page. Challenge the children to find a start number and an add number that will reach the correct finish number. See also the note on page 59.

Hungry mice

- Add the numbers on the mice.
- Write the total on the cheese.

- Choose your own numbers.
- Write the total on the cheese.

Teachers' note Provide copies of the 100-grid and 100-track on pages 63 and 64. Using both the grid and the track will help to support pupils' understanding of counting patterns. Ensure the children are aware of the simplicity of 'adding on 10' patterns. In the extension activity, encourage them to try larger starting numbers than the 'teens'.

Horse race

- **Write the totals.**

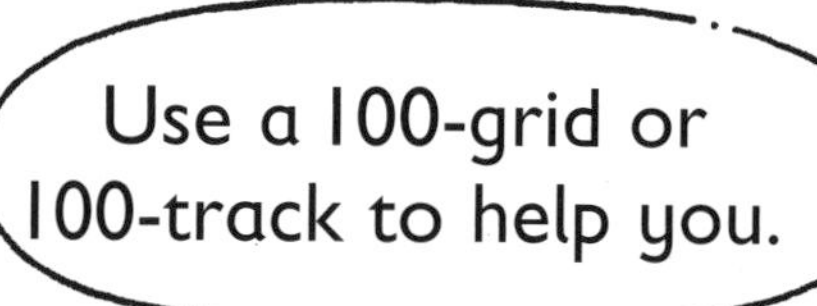
Use a 100-grid or 100-track to help you.

A

10 + 11 = 21 | 17 + 12 = | 12 + 13 =

B

14 + 12 = | 12 + 12 = | 11 + 11 =

C

12 + 15 = | 15 + 13 = | 13 + 14 =

D

11 + 12 = | 15 + 12 = | 16 + 11 =

- **Colour red fences worth** less than 24**.**
- **Colour blue fences worth** between 24 and 26**.**
- **Colour yellow fences worth** more than 26**.**
- **Horses will only jump over blue and yellow fences. Which horse will finish the race?** ☐

Teachers' note Provide copies of the 100-grid and 100-track on pages 63 and 64. Using both the grid and the track will help to reinforce the idea of using counting skills to add. Note that none of these additions involves crossing a 'tens' boundary.

100-grid

0	1	2	3	4	5	6	7	8	9
10	11	12	13	14	15	16	17	18	19
20	21	22	23	24	25	26	27	28	29
30	31	32	33	34	35	36	37	38	39
40	41	42	43	44	45	46	47	48	49
50	51	52	53	54	55	56	57	58	59
60	61	62	63	64	65	66	67	68	69
70	71	72	73	74	75	76	77	78	79
80	81	82	83	84	85	86	87	88	89
90	91	92	93	94	95	96	97	98	99
100									

100-track

0
1
2
3
4
5
6
7
8
9
10
19
18
17
16
15
14
13
12
11
20
21
22
23
24
25
26
27
28
29
30
39
38
37
36
35
34
33
32
31
40
41
42
43
44
45
46
47
48
49
50
59
58
57
56
55
54
53
52
51
60
61
62
63
64
65
66
67
68
69
70
79
78
77
76
75
74
73
72
71
80
81
82
83
84
85
86
87
88
89
90
99
98
97
96
95
94
93
92
91
100